Library Edition

———

# THE WIT AND HUMOR
# OF AMERICA

In Ten Volumes

VOL. I

MARSHALL P. WILDER

Drawing from photo by Marceau

# THE
# WIT AND HUMOR
# OF AMERICA

EDITED BY
## MARSHALL P. WILDER

*Volume I*

## Funk & Wagnalls Company
New York and London

# CONTENTS

# CONTENTS

COMPLETE INDEX AT END OF VOLUME X.

# FOREWORD·

## Embodying a Few Remarks on the Gentle Art of Laugh-Making.

### BY

## Marshall P. Wilder.

———

Happiness and laughter are two of the most beautiful things in the world, for they are of the few that are purely unselfish. Laughter is not for yourself, but for others. When people are happy they present a cheerful spirit, which finds its reflection in every one they meet, for happiness is as contagious as a yawn. Of all the emotions, laughter is the most versatile, for it plays equally well the role of either parent or child to happiness.

Then can we say too much in praise of the men who make us laugh? God never gave a man a greater gift than the power to make others laugh, unless it is the privilege of laughing himself. We honor, revere, admire our great soldiers, statesmen, and men of letters, but we love the man who makes us laugh.

No other man to-day enjoys to such an extent the close personal affection, individual yet national, that is given to Mr. Samuel L. Clemens. He is ours, he is one of us, we have a personal pride in him—dear "Mark

Twain," the beloved child of the American nation. And it was through our laughter that he won our love.

He is the exponent of the typically American style of fun-making, the humorous story. I asked Mr. Clemens one day if he could remember the first money he ever earned. With his inimitable drawl he said:

"Yes, Marsh, it was at school. All boys had the habit of going to school in those days, and they hadn't any more respect for the desks than they had for the teachers. There was a rule in our school that any boy marring his desk, either with pencil or knife, would be chastised publicly before the whole school, or pay a fine of five dollars. Besides the rule, there was a ruler; I knew it because I had felt it; it was a darned hard one, too. One day I had to tell my father that I had broken the rule, and had to pay a fine or take a public whipping; and he said:

"'Sam, it would be too bad to have the name of Clemens disgraced before the whole school, so I'll pay the fine. But I don't want you to lose anything, so come upstairs.'

"I went upstairs with father, and he was for-*giving* me. I came downstairs with the feeling in one hand and the five dollars in the other, and decided that as I'd been punished once, and got used to it, I wouldn't mind taking the other licking at school. So I did, and I kept the five dollars. That was the first money I ever earned."

The humorous story as expounded by Mark Twain, Artemus Ward, and Robert J. Burdette, is purely American. Artemus Ward could get laughs out of nothing, by mixing the absurd and the unexpected, and then backing the combination with a solemn face and earnest manner. For instance, he was fond of such incongruous statements as: "I once knew a man in New Zealand who hadn't a tooth in his head," here he would pause for some time, look reminiscent, and continue: "and yet he could beat a base-drum better than any man I ever knew."

Robert J. Burdette, who wrote columns of capital humor for *The Burlington Hawkeye* and told stories superbly, on his first visit to New York was spirited to a notable club, where he told stories leisurely until half the hearers ached with laughter, and the other half were threatened with apoplexy. Everyone present declared it the red-letter night of the club, and members who had missed it came around and demanded the stories at second hand. Some efforts were made to oblige them, but without avail, for the tellers had twisted their recollections of the stories into jokes, and they didn't sound right, so a committee hunted the town for Burdette to help them out of their difficulty.

Humor is the kindliest method of laugh-making. Wit and satire are ancient, but humor, it has been claimed, belongs to modern times. A certain type of story, having a sudden and terse conclusion to a direct statement, has been labeled purely American. For instance: "Willie Jones loaded and fired a cannon yesterday. The funeral will be to-morrow." But the truth is, it is older than America; it is very venerable. If you will turn to the twelfth verse of the sixteenth chapter of II. Chronicles, you will read:

"And Asa in the thirty-ninth year of his reign was diseased in his feet, until his disease was exceeding great; yet in his disease he sought not the Lord, but turned to the physicians—and Asa slept with his fathers."

Bill Nye was a sturdy and persistent humorist of so

good a sort that he never could help being humorous, yet there was never a sting in his jokes. Gentle raillery was the severest thing he ever attempted, and even this he did with so genial a smile and so merry an eye, that a word of his friendly chaffing was worth more than any amount of formal praise.

Few of the great world's great despatches contained so much wisdom in so few words as Nye's historic wire from Washington:

"My friends and money gave out at 3 A.M."

Eugene Field, the lover of little children, and the self-confessed bibliomaniac, gives us still another sort of laugh—the tender, indulgent sort. Nothing could be finer than the gentle reminiscence of "Long Ago," a picture of the lost kingdom of boyhood, which for all its lightness holds a pathos that clutches one in the throat.

And yet this writer of delicate and subtle humor, this master of tender verse, had a keen and nimble wit. An ambitious poet once sent him a poem to read entitled "Why do I live?" and Field immediately wrote back: "Because you sent your poem by mail."

Laughter is one of the best medicines in the world, and though some people would make you force it down with a spoon, there is no doubt that it is a splendid tonic and awakens the appetite for happiness.

Colonel Ingersoll wrote on his photograph which adorns my home: "To the man who knows that mirth is medicine and laughter lengthens life."

Abraham Lincoln, that divinely tender man, believed that fun was an intellectual impetus, for he read Artemus Ward to his Cabinet before reading his famous emancipation proclamation, and laying down his book marked the place to resume.

# FOREWORD

Joel Chanler Harris, whose delightful stories of negro life hold such a high place in American literature, told me a story of an old negro who claimed that a sense of humor was necessary to happiness in married life. He said:

" I met a poor old darkey one day, pushing a wheel-barrow loaded with cooking utensils and household effects. Seeing me looking curiously at him, he shook his head and said:

" 'I cain't stand her no longer, boss, I jes' nash'ully cain't stand her no longer.'

" 'What's the matter, uncle?' I inquired.

" 'Well, you see, suh, she ain't got no idee o' fun— she won't take a joke nohow. The other night I went home, an' I been takin' a little jes' to waam ma heart— das all, jes to waam ma heart—an' I got to de fence, an' tried to climb it. I got on de top, an' thar I stays; I couldn't git one way or t'other. Then a gem'en comes along, an' I says, "Would you min' givin' me a push?" He says, "Which way you want to go?" I says, "Either way— don't make no dif'unce, jes' so I git off de fence, for hit's pow'ful oncom'fable up yer." So he give me a push, an' sont me over to'ard ma side, an' I went home. Then I want sum'in t' eat, an' my ol' 'ooman she wouldn' git it fo' me, an' so, jes' fo' a joke, das all—jes' a joke, I hit 'er awn de haid. But would you believe it, she couldn't take a joke. She tu'n aroun', an' sir, she sail inter me sum'in' scan'lous! I didn' do nothin', 'cause I feelin' kind o' weak jes' then — an' so I made up ma min' I wasn' goin' to stay with her. Dis mawnin' she gone out washin', an' I jes' move right out. Hit's no use tryin' to live with a 'ooman who cain't take a joke!' "

From the poems of Thomas Bailey Aldrich to George Ade's Fables in Slang is a far cry, but one is as typical a style of humor as the other. Ade's is the more distinctly original, for he not only created the style, but another language. The aptness of its turns, and the marvelous way in which he hit the bull's-eye of human foibles and weaknesses lifted him into instantaneous popularity. A famous *bon mot* of George Ade's which has been quoted threadbare, but which serves excellently to illustrate his native wit, is his remark about a suit of clothes which the tailor assured him he could *n ever* wear out. He said when he put them on he didn't *dare* to.

From the laughter-makers pure and simple, we come to those who, while acknowledging the cloud, yet see the silver lining—the exponents of the smile through tears.

The best of these, Frank L. Stanton, has beautifully said:

> "This world that we're a-livin' in
> Is mighty hard to beat;
> With every rose you get a thorn,
> But ain't the roses sweet?"

He does not deny the thorns, but calls attention to the sweetness of the roses—a gospel of compensation that speaks to the heart of all; kind words of cheer to the weary traveler.

Such a philosopher was the kind-hearted and sympathetic Irish boy who, walking along with the parish priest, met a weary organ-grinder, who asked how far it was to the next town. The boy answered, "Four miles." The priest remonstrated:

Why, Mike, how can you deceive him so? You know it is eight."

"Well, your riverence," said the good-natured fellow, "I saw how tired he was, and I wanted to kape his courage up. If I'd told him the truth, he'd have been down-hearted intirely!"

# FOREWORD

This is really a jolly old world, and people are very apt to find just what they are looking for. If they are looking for happiness, the best way to find it is to try to give it to others. If a man goes around with a face as long as a wet day, perfectly certain that he is going to be kicked, he is seldom disappointed.

A typical exponent of the tenderly human, the tearfully humorous, is James Whitcomb Riley — a name to conjure with. Only mention it to anyone, and note the spark of interest, the smiling sigh, the air of gentle retrospection into which he will fall. There is a poem for each and every one, that commends itself for some special reason, and holds such power of memory or sentiment as sends it straight into the heart, to remain there treasured and unforgotten.

In these volumes are selections from the pen of all whom I have mentioned, as well as many more, including a number by the clever women humorists, of whom America is justly proud.

It is with pride and pleasure that I acknowledge the honor done me in being asked to introduce this company of fun-makers — such a goodly number that space permits the mention of but a few. But we cannot have too much or even enough of anything so good or so necessary as the literature that makes us laugh. In that regard we are like a little friend of Mr. Riley's.

The Hoosier poet, as everyone knows, is the devoted friend, companion, and singer of children. He has a habit of taking them on wild orgies where they are turned loose in a candy store and told to do their worst. This particular young lady had been allowed to choose all the sorts of candy she liked until her mouth, both arms, and her pockets were full. Just as they got to the door to go out, she hung back, and when Mr. Riley stooped over asking her what was the matter, she whispered:

"Don't you think it smells like ice cream?"

Poems, stories, humorous articles, fables, and fairy tales are offered for your choice, with subjects as diverse as the styles; but however the laugh is gained, in whatever fashion the jest is delivered, the laugh-maker is a public benefactor, for laughter is the salt of life, and keeps the whole dish sweet.

Merrily yours,<br>MARSHALL P. WILDER.

ATLANTIC CITY, 1908.

# ACKNOWLEDGMENT

Acknowledgment is due to the following publishers, whose permission was cordially granted to reprint selections which appear in this collection of American humor.

AINSLEE'S MAGAZINE for "Not According to Schedule," by Mary Stewart Cutting.

THE HENRY ALTEMUS COMPANY for "The New Version," by William J. Lampton.

THE AMERICAN PUBLISHING COMPANY for "How We Bought a Sewin' Machine and Organ," from *Josiah Allen's Wife as a P. A. and P. I.,* by Marietta Holley.

D. APPLETON & COMPANY for "The Recruit," from *With the Band,* by Robert W. Chambers.

E. H. BACON & COMPANY for "The V-a-s-e" and "A Concord Love-Song," from *The V-a-s-e and Other Bric-a-Brac,* by James Jeffrey Roche.

THE H. M. CALDWELL COMPANY for "Yes" and "Disappointment," from *In Bohemia,* by John Boyle O'Reilly.

THE COLVER PUBLISHING HOUSE for "The Crimson Cord," by Ellis Parker Butler, and "A Ballade of the 'How to' Books," by John James Davies, from *The American Illustrated Magazine.*

THE CROWELL PUBLISHING COMPANY for "Familiar Authors at Work," by Hayden Carruth, from *The Woman's Home Companion.*

THE CURTIS PUBLISHING COMPANY for "The Love Sonnets of a Husband," by Maurice Smiley, and "Cheer for the Consumer," by Nixon Waterman, from *The Saturday Evening Post.*

ix

# ACKNOWLEDGMENT

DeWolfe, Fiske & Company for "Grandma Keeler Gets Grandpa Ready for Sunday-School," from *Cape Cod Folks,* by Sarah P. McLean Greene.

Dick & Fitzgerald for "The Thompson Street Poker Club," from *The Thompson Street Poker Club,* by Henry Guy Carleton.

G. W. Dillingham Company for "The Tower of London" and "Science and Natural History," by Charles Farrar Browne ("Artemus Ward"); "The Muskeeter," from *Farmer's Alminax,* and "Laffing," from *Josh Billings: His Works,* by Henry W. Shaw ("Josh Billings"); and for "John Henry in a Street Car," from *John Henry,* by George V. Hobart ("Hugh McHugh").

Dodd, Mead & Company for "The Rhyme of the Chivalrous Shark," "The Forbearance of the Admiral," "The Dutiful Mariner," "The Meditations of a Mariner" and "The Boat that Ain't," from *Nautical Lays of a Landsman,* by Wallace Irwin.

The Duquesne Distributing Company for "The Grand Opera," from *Billy Baxter's Letters,* by William J. Kountz, Jr.

Paul Elder & Company for Sonnets I, VIII, IX, XII, XIV, XXI, from *The Love Sonnets of a Hoodlum,* by Wallace Irwin.

Everybody's Magazine for "The Strike of One," by Elliott Flower; "The Wolf's Holiday," by Caroline Duer; "A Mother of Four," by Juliet Wilbor Tompkins; "The Weddin'," by Jennie Betts Hartswick, and "A Double-Dyed Deceiver," by Sydney Porter ("O. Henry").

The Federal Book Company for "Budge and Toddie," from *Helen's Babies,* by John Habberton.

Fords, Howard & Hurlburt, for "The Deacon's Trout," from *Norwood,* by Henry Ward Beecher.

# ACKNOWLEDGMENT

Fox, Duffield & Company for "The Paintermine," "The Octopussycat," "The Welsh Rabbittern," "The Bumblebeaver," "The Wild Boarder," from *Mixed Beasts*, by Kenyon Cox; "The Lost Inventor," "Niagara Be Dammed," "The Ballad of Grizzly Gulch," "A Letter from Home," "Crankidoxology" and "Fall Styles in Faces," from *At the Sign of the Dollar*, by Wallace Irwin, and a selection from *The Golfer's Rubaiyat*, by Henry W. Boynton.

The Harvard Lampoon for "A Lay of Ancient Rome," by Thomas Ybarra.

Henry Holt & Company for "Araminta and the Automobile," from *Cheerful Americans*, by Charles Battell Loomis.

Houghton, Mifflin & Company for "A Letter from Mr. Biggs," from *The Story of a Country Town*, by E. W. Howe; "The Notary of Perigueux," from *Outre-Mer*, by Henry Wadsworth Longfellow; "A Nautical Ballad," from *Davy and the Goblin*, by Charles E. Carryl; "The Spring Beauties," from *The Ride to the Lady*, by Helen Avery Cone; "Praise-God Barebones," from *Songs and Lyrics*, by Ellen M. Hutchinson-Cortissoz; "Fable," from *Poems*, by Ralph Waldo Emerson; "The Owl Critic" and "Cæsar's Quiet Lunch with Cicero," from *Ballads and Other Poems*, by James T. Fields; "The Menagerie," from *Poems*, by William Vaughn Moody; "The Briefless Barrister," "Comic Miseries," "A Reflective Retrospect," "How the Money Goes," "The Coquette," "Icarus," "Teaching by Example," from *Poems*, by John Godfrey Saxe; "My Honey, My Love," by Joel Chandler Harris; "Banty Tim," "The Mystery of Gilgal" and "Distichs," from *Poems*, by John Hay; "The Deacon's Masterpiece, or The Wonderful One Hoss Shay," "The Height of the Ridiculous," "Evening, By a Tailor," "Lat-

# ACKNOWLEDGMENT

ter Day Warnings," and "Contentment," from *Poems,* by Oliver Wendell Holmes; two selections from *The Autocrat of the Breakfast Table,* by Oliver Wendell Holmes, and "Dislikes,"_ from *The Poet at the Breakfast Table,* by Oliver Wendell Holmes; "Plain Language from Truthful James," and "The Society Upon the Stanislaus," from *Poems,* by Bret Harte; "Melons," from *Mrs. Skaggs' Husbands and Other Sketches,* by Bret Harte; "The Courtin'," "A Letter from Mr. Ezekiel Biglow" and "What Mr. Robinson Thinks," from *Poems,* by James Russell Lowell; "The Chief Mate," from *Fireside Travels,* by James Russell Lowell; "A Night in a Rocking Chair" and "A Rival Entertainment," from *Haphazard,* by Kate Field; "Mrs. Johnson," from *Suburban Sketches,* by William Dean Howells; "Garden Ethics," from *My Summer in a Garden,* by Charles Dudley Warner; "Our Nearest Neighbor," from *Marjorie Daw and Other Stories,* by Thomas Bailey Aldrich; "Simon Starts in the World" (J. J. Hooper), "The Duluth Speech" (J. Proctor Knott), "Bill Arp on Litigation" (C. H. Smith), "Assault and Battery" (J. G. Baldwin), "How Ruby Played" (G. W. Bagby), from *Oddities of Southern Life,* edited by Henry Watterson; "The Demon of the Study," from *Poems,* by John Greenleaf Whittier; "The Old Maid's House: in Plan," from *An Old Maid's Paradise,* by Elizabeth Stuart Phelps; "Dum Vivimus Vigilamus," "What She Said About It," "Dictum Sapienti," "The Lost Word" and "Abou Ben Butler," from *Poems,* by Charles Henry Webb ("John Paul"); "Chad's Story of the Goose" and "Colonel Carter's Story of the Postmaster," from *Colonel Carter of Cartersville,* by F. Hopkinson Smith; "The British Matron," from *Our Old Home,* by Nathaniel Hawthorne; "As Good as a Play," from *Stories from My Attic,* by Horace E. Scudder; "The Pettibone Lineage,"

# ACKNOWLEDGMENT

by James T. Fields; "The Experiences of the A. C.," by Bayard Taylor; "Eve's Daughter," by Edward Rowland Sill, and "The Diamond Wedding," by Edmund Clarence Stedman.

WILLIAM R. JENKINS for "It Is Time to Begin to Conclude," from *Soldier Songs and Love Songs*, by Alexander H. Laidlaw.

JOHN LANE COMPANY for "The Invisible Prince," from *Comedies and Errors*, by Henry Harland.

LIFE PUBLISHING COMPANY for "Hard," "Enough" and "Desolation," from *In Merry Measure*, by Tom Masson; "A Branch Library" and "Table Manners," from *Tomfoolery*, by James Montgomery Flagg; "The Sonnet of the Lovable Lass and the Plethoric Dad," by J. W. Foley; "Thoughts for an Easter Morning," by Wallace Irwin; "Suppressed Chapters," by Carolyn Wells; "The Conscientious Curate and the Beauteous Ballad Girl," by William Russell Rose, and "A Poe-'em of Passion," by Charles F. Lummis.

LIPPINCOTT'S MAGAZINE for "The Modern Farmer," by Jack Appleton; "The Wicked Zebra" and "The Happy Land," by Frank Roe Batchelder; "A Mothers' Meeting," by Madeline Bridges; "The Final Choice" and "A Daniel Come to Judgment," by Edmund Vance Cooke; "The Co-operative Housekeepers" and "Her 'Angel' Father," by Elliott Flower; "Wasted Opportunities," by Roy Farrell Greene; "The Auto Rubaiyat," by Reginald W. Kauffman; "It Pays to be Happy" and "Victory," by Tom Masson; "Is It I?" by Warwick S. Price; "Johnny's Lessons," by Carroll Watson Rankin; "Her Brother: Enfant Terrible" and "Trouble-Proof," by E. L. Sabin; "A Bookworm's Plaint," by Clinton Scollard; "Nothin' Done," by S. S. Stinson, and "Uncle Bentley and the Roosters," by Hayden Carruth.

# ACKNOWLEDGMENT

LITTLE, BROWN & COMPANY for "Elizabeth Eliza Writes a Paper," from *The Peterkin Papers*, by Lucretia P. Hale; "The Skeleton in the Closet," by Edward Everett Hale, and "The Wolf at Susan's Door," from *The Wolf at Susan's Door and Mrs. Lathrop's Love Affair*, by Anne Warner.

LOTHROP, LEE & SHEPARD for "A Letter," from *Swingin' Round the Circle*, by David Ross Locke ("P. V. Nasby"); "A Cable Car Preacher" and "The Prayer of Cyrus Brown," from *Dreams in Homespun*, by Sam Walter Foss; "He Wanted to Know," "Hullo!" and "She Talked," from *Back Country Poems*, by Sam Walter Foss; "Mr. Stiver's Horse" and "After the Funeral," from the works of James M. Bailey (The Danbury News Man); "Yawcob Strauss," "Der Oak und der Vine," "To Bary Jade" and "Shonny Schwartz," from *Leetle Yawcob Strauss*, by Charles Follen Adams; "The Coupon Bonds" and "Darius Greene," from the works of J. T. Trowbridge, and Chapters VII, IX, XVI, XX, XXI, from "Partingtonian Patchwork," by B. P. Shillaber.

THE S. S. McCLURE COMPANY and McCLURE, PHILLIPS & COMPANY for "Morris and the Honorable Tim," from *Little Citizens*, by Myra Kelly.

A. C. McCLURG & COMPANY for "Simple English," from *At the Sign of the Ginger Jar*, by Ray Clarke Rose, and "Ye Legende of Sir Yroncladde," by Wilbur D. Nesbit, from *The Athlete's Garland*.

DAVID McKAY for "Hans Breitmann's Party," "Breitmann and the Turners," "Ballad," "Breitmann in Politics" and "Love Song," from *Hans Breitmann's Ballads*, by Charles Godfrey Leland, and "A Boston Ballad," from *Leaves of Grass*, by Walt Whitman.

THE MACMILLAN COMPANY for "In a State of Sin," from *The Virginian*, by Owen Wister.

# ACKNOWLEDGMENT

THE MONARCH BOOK COMPANY for "The Apostasy of William Dodge," from *The Seekers,* by Stanley Waterloo.

THE FRANK A. MUNSEY COMPANY for "An Educational Project" and "The Woman-Hater Reformed," by Roy Farrell Greene; "The Trial That Job Missed," by Kennett Harris; "The Education of Grandpa," by Wallace Irwin; "An Improved Calendar," by Tudor Jenks.

SMALL, MAYNARD & COMPANY for "Mr Dooley on Gold Seeking," "Mr. Dooley on Expert Testimony," "Mr. Dooley on Golf," "Mr. Dooley on Football," "Mr. Dooley on Reform Candidates," from *Mr. Dooley in Peace and War,* by Finley Peter Dunne; "E. O. R. S. W." from *Alphabet of Celebrities,* by Oliver Herford; "A Letter," from *The Letters of a Self-Made Merchant to His Son,* by George Horace Lorimer; "Vive La Bagatelle" and "Willy and the Lady," from *A Gage of Youth,* by Gelett Burgess; "When the Allegash Drive Goes Through," from *Pine Tree Ballads,* by Holman F. Day; "Had a Set of Double Teeth," from *Up in Maine,* by Holman F. Day; "Similar Cases," from *In This Our World,* by Charlotte Perkins Gilman; "Barney McGee," by Richard Hovey, from *More Songs from Vagabondia;* "A Modern Eclogue," "The Sceptics," "A Staccato to O le Lupe," "A Spring Feeling," "Her Valentine" and "In Philistia," by Bliss Carman, from *Last Songs from Vagabondia,* and "Vive la Bagatelle," "A Cavalier's Valentine" and "Holly Song," from *Hills of Song,* by Clinton Scollard.

THE MUTUAL BOOK COMPANY for "James and Reginald" and "The Story of the Two Friars," from *The Tribune Primer,* by Eugene Field.

THE ORANGE JUDD COMPANY for "Spelling Down

the Master," from *The Hoosier Schoolmaster,* by Edward Eggleston.

JAMES POTT & COMPANY for "The Gusher," from *I've Been Thinking,* by Charles Battell Loomis.

G. P. PUTNAM'S SONS for "When Albani Sang" and "The Stove Pipe Hole," from *The Habitant,* by William Henry Drummond; "National Philosophy," from *The Voyageur,* by William Henry Drummond; "The Siege of Djklxprwbz," "Grizzly-gru," "He and She," "The Jackpot," "A Shining Mark," "The Reason," "Pass" and "The Whisperer," from *The Rhymes of Ironquill,* by Eugene F. Ware, and "A Family Horse," from *The Sparrowgrass Papers,* by Frederick S. Cozzens.

RAND, McNALLY & COMPANY for "An Arkansas Planter," from *An Arkansas Planter,* by Opie Read.

A. M. ROBERTSON for "The Drayman," from *Songs of Bohemia,* by Daniel O'Connell.

R. H. RUSSELL for "Mr. Carteret and His Fellow-Americans Abroad," by David Gray, from *The Metropolitan Magazine.*

THE SMART SET PUBLISHING COMPANY for "An Evening Musicale," by May Isabel Fisk, from *The Smart Set.*

THE FREDERICK A. STOKES COMPANY for "Colonel Sterett's Panther Hunt," from *Wolfville Nights,* by Alfred Henry Lewis; "The Bohemians of Boston," "The Purple Cow" and "Nonsense Verses," from *The Burgess Nonsense Book,* by Gelett Burgess, and "My Grandmother's Turkey-tail Fan," "Little Bopeep and Little Boy Blue" and "My Sweetheart," by Samuel Minturn Peck.

THE TANDY-WHEELER PUBLISHING COMPANY for "Utah," "A New Year Idyl," "The Warrior," "Lost

# ACKNOWLEDGMENT

Chords" and "The Advertiser," from *A Little Book of Tribune Verse,* by Eugene Field.

THOMPSON & THOMAS for "The Grammatical Boy," by Edgar Wilson Nye ("Bill Nye").

THE A. WESSELS COMPANY for "The Dying Gag," by James L. Ford.

M. WITMARK & SONS for "Walk," from *Jim Marshall's New Pianner,* by William Devere.

Special thanks are due to George Ade, Wallace Bruce Amsbary, John Kendrick Bangs, H. W. Boynton, Gelett Burgess, Ellis Parker Butler, Hayden Carruth, Robert W. Chambers, Charles Heber Clarke, Joseph I. C. Clarke, Mary Stewart Cutting, John James Davies, Caroline Duer, Mrs. Edward Eggleston, May Isabel Fisk, Elliott Flower, James L. Ford, David Gray, Sarah P. McLean Greene, Jennie Betts Hartswick, William Dean Howells, Wallace Irwin, Charles F. Johnson, S. E. Kiser, A. H. Laidlaw, Alfred Henry Lewis, Charles B. Lewis, Charles Battell Loomis, Charles F. Lummis, T. L. Masson, William Vaughn Moody, R. K. Munkittrick, W. D. Nesbit, Meredith Nicholson, Alden Charles Noble, Samuel Minturn Peck, Sydney Porter, Wallace Rice, James Whitcomb Riley, Doane Robinson, Henry A. Shute, F. Hopkinson Smith, Harriet Prescott Spofford, Howard V. Sutherland, John B. Tabb, Bert Leston Taylor, Juliet Wilbor Tompkins, Elizabeth Stuart Phelps Ward, Eugene F. Ware, Anne Warner French and Stanley Waterloo for permission to reprint selections from their works and for many valuable suggestions.

# THE WIT AND HUMOR
# OF AMERICA

## MELONS

BY BRET HARTE

As I do not suppose the most gentle of readers will believe that anybody's sponsors in baptism ever wilfully assumed the responsibility of such a name, I may as well state that I have reason to infer that Melons was simply the nickname of a small boy I once knew. If he had any other, I never knew it.

Various theories were often projected by me to account for this strange cognomen. His head, which was covered with a transparent down, like that which clothes very small chickens, plainly permitting the scalp to show through, to an imaginative mind might have suggested that succulent vegetable. That his parents, recognizing some poetical significance in the fruits of the season, might have given this name to an August child, was an oriental explanation. That from his infancy, he was fond of indulging in melons, seemed on the whole the most likely, particularly as Fancy was not bred in McGinnis's Court. He dawned upon me as Melons. His proximity was indicated by shrill, youthful voices, as "Ah, Melons!" or playfully, "Hi, Melons!" or authoritatively, "You Melons!"

McGinnis's Court was a democratic expression of some obstinate and radical property-holder. Occupying a limited space between two fashionable thoroughfares, it refused to conform to circumstances, but sturdily paraded its unkempt glories, and frequently asserted itself in ungrammatical language. My window—a rear room on the ground floor—in this way derived blended light and shadow from the court. So low was the window-sill that, had I been the least disposed to somnambulism, it would have broken out under such favorable auspices, and I should have haunted McGinnis's Court. My speculations as to the origin of the court were not altogether gratuitous, for by means of this window I once saw the Past, as through a glass darkly. It was a Celtic shadow that early one morning obstructed my ancient lights. It seemed to belong to an individual with a pea-coat, a stubby pipe, and bristling beard. He was gazing intently at the court, resting on a heavy cane, somewhat in the way that heroes dramatically visit the scenes of their boyhood. As there was little of architectural beauty in the court, I came to the conclusion that it was McGinnis looking after his property. The fact that he carefully kicked a broken bottle out of the road somewhat strengthened me in the opinion. But he presently walked away, and the court knew him no more. He probably collected his rents by proxy—if he collected them at all.

Beyond Melons, of whom all this is purely introductory, there was little to interest the most sanguine and hopeful nature. In common with all such localities, a great deal of washing was done, in comparison with the visible results. There was always some thing whisking on the line, and always some thing whisking through the court, that looked as if it ought to be there. A fish-geranium—of all plants kept for the recreation of mankind, certainly the greatest illusion—straggled under the window. Through its dusty leaves I caught the first glance of Melons.

2

His age was about seven. He looked older from the venerable whiteness of his head, and it was impossible to conjecture his size, as he always wore clothes apparently belonging to some shapely youth of nineteen. A pair of pantaloons, that, when sustained by a single suspender, completely equipped him, formed his every-day suit. How, with this lavish superfluity of clothing, he managed to perform the surprising gymnastic feats it has been my privilege to witness, I have never been able to tell. His "turning the crab," and other minor dislocations, were always attended with success. It was not an unusual sight at any hour of the day to find Melons suspended on a line, or to see his venerable head appearing above the roofs of the outhouses. Melons knew the exact height of every fence in the vicinity, its facilities for scaling, and the possibility of seizure on the other side. His more peaceful and quieter amusements consisted in dragging a disused boiler by a large string, with hideous outcries, to imaginary fires.

Melons was not gregarious in his habits. A few youth of his own age sometimes called upon him, but they eventually became abusive, and their visits were more strictly predatory incursions for old bottles and junk which formed the staple of McGinnis's Court. Overcome by loneliness one day, Melons inveigled a blind harper into the court. For two hours did that wretched man prosecute his unhallowed calling, unrecompensed, and going round and round the court, apparently under the impression that it was some other place, while Melons surveyed him from an adjoining fence with calm satisfaction. It was this absence of conscientious motives that brought Melons into disrepute with his aristocratic neighbors. Orders were issued that no child of wealthy and pious parentage should play with him. This man-

3

date, as a matter of course, invested Melons with a fascinating interest to them. Admiring glances were cast at Melons from nursery windows. Baby fingers beckoned to him. Invitations to tea (on wood and pewter) were lisped to him from aristocratic back-yards. It was evident he was looked upon as a pure and noble being, untrammelled by the conventionalities of parentage, and physically as well as mentally exalted above them. One afternoon an unusual commotion prevailed in the vicinity of McGinnis's Court. Looking from my window I saw Melons perched on the roof of a stable, pulling up a rope by which one "Tommy," an infant scion of an adjacent and wealthy house, was suspended in mid-air. In vain the female relatives of Tommy, congregated in the back-yard, expostulated with Melons; in vain the unhappy father shook his fist at him. Secure in his position, Melons redoubled his exertions and at last landed Tommy on the roof. Then it was that the humiliating fact was disclosed that Tommy had been acting in collusion with Melons. He grinned delightedly back at his parents, as if "by merit raised to that bad eminence." Long before the ladder arrived that was to succor him, he became the sworn ally of Melons, and, I regret to say, incited by the same audacious boy, "chaffed" his own flesh and blood below him. He was eventually taken, though, of course, Melons escaped. But Tommy was restricted to the window after that, and the companionship was limited to "Hi Melons!" and "You Tommy!" and Melons to all practical purposes, lost him forever. I looked afterward to see some signs of sorrow on Melons's part, but in vain; he buried his grief, if he had any, somewhere in his one voluminous garment.

At about this time my opportunities of knowing Melons became more extended. I was engaged in filling a void in the Literature of the Pacific Coast. As this void was a pretty large one, and as I was informed that the Pacific Coast languished under it, I set apart two hours each day to this work of filling in. It was necessary that I should adopt a methodical system, so I retired from the world and locked myself in my room at a certain hour each day, after coming from my office. I then carefully drew out my portfolio and read what I had written the day before. This would suggest some alterations, and I would carefully rewrite it. During this operation I would turn to consult a book of reference, which invariably proved extremely interesting and attractive. It would generally suggest another and better method of "filling in." Turning this method over reflectively in my mind, I would finally commence the new method which I eventually abandoned for the original plan. At this time I would become convinced that my exhausted faculties demanded a cigar. The operation of lighting a cigar usually suggested that a little quiet reflection and meditation would be of service to me, and I always allowed myself to be guided by prudential instincts. Eventually, seated by my window, as before stated, Melons asserted himself. Though our conversation rarely went further than "Hello, Mister!" and "Ah, Melons!" a vagabond instinct we felt in common implied a communion deeper than words. In this spiritual commingling the time passed, often beguiled by gymnastics on the fence or line (always with an eye to my window) until dinner was announced and I found a more practical void required my attention. An unlooked-for incident drew us in closer relation.

A sea-faring friend just from a tropical voyage had presented me with a bunch of bananas. They were not quite ripe, and I hung them before my window to mature in the sun of McGinnis's Court, whose forcing qualities were remarkable. In the mysteriously mingled odors of ship and shore which they diffused throughout my room, there was lingering reminiscence of low latitudes. But even that joy was fleeting and evanescent: they never reached maturity.

Coming home one day, as I turned the corner of that fashionable thoroughfare before alluded to, I met a small boy eating a banana. There was nothing remarkable in that, but as I neared McGinnis's Court I presently met another small boy, also eating a banana. A third small boy engaged in a like occupation obtruded a painful co-incidence upon my mind. I leave the psychological reader to determine the exact co-relation between the circumstance and the sickening sense of loss that overcame me on witnessing it. I reached my room—the bananas were gone.

There was but one that knew of their existence, but one who frequented my window, but one capable of gymnastic effort to procure them, and that was—I blush to say it—Melons. Melons the depredator—Melons, despoiled by larger boys of his ill-gotten booty, or reckless and indiscreetly liberal; Melons—now a fugitive on some neighborhood house-top. I lit a cigar, and, drawing my chair to the window, sought surcease of sorrow in the contemplation of the fish-geranium. In a few moments something white passed my window at about the level of the edge. There was no mistaking that hoary head, which now represented to me only aged iniquity. It was Melons, that venerable, juvenile hypocrite.

He affected not to observe me, and would have withdrawn quietly, but that horrible fascination which causes the murderer to revisit the scene of his crime, impelled him toward my window. I smoked calmly, and gazed at him without speaking. He walked several times up and down the court with a half-rigid, half-belligerent expression of eye and shoulder, intended to represent the carelessness of innocence.

Once or twice he stopped, and putting his arms their whole length into his capacious trousers, gazed with some interest at the additional width they thus acquired. Then he whistled. The singular conflicting conditions of John Brown's body and soul were at that time beginning to attract the attention of youth, and Melons's performance of that melody was always remarkable. But to-day he whistled falsely and shrilly between his teeth. At last he met my eye. He winced slightly, but recovered himself, and going to the fence, stood for a few moments on his hands, with his bare feet quivering in the air. Then he turned toward me and threw out a conversational preliminary.

"They is a cirkis"—said Melons gravely, hanging with his back to the fence and his arms twisted around the palings—"a cirkis over yonder!"—indicating the locality with his foot—"with hosses, and hossback riders. They is a man wot rides six hosses to onct—six hosses to onct—and nary saddle"—and he paused in expectation.

Even this equestrian novelty did not affect me. I still kept a fixed gaze on Melons's eye, and he began to tremble and visibly shrink in his capacious garment. Some other desperate means—conversation with Melons was always a desperate means—must be resorted to. He recommenced more artfully.

"Do you know Carrots?"

I had a faint remembrance of a boy of that euphonious name, with scarlet hair, who was a playmate and persecutor of Melons. But I said nothing.

"Carrots is a bad boy. Killed a policeman onct. Wears a dirk knife in his boots, saw him to-day looking in your windy."

I felt that this must end here. I rose sternly and addressed Melons.

"Melons, this is all irrelevant and impertinent to the case. *You* took those bananas. Your proposition regarding Carrots, even if I were inclined to accept it as credible information, does not alter the material issue. You took those bananas. The offense under the Statutes of California is felony. How far Carrots may have been accessory to the fact either before or after, is not my intention at present to discuss. The act is complete. Your present conduct shows the *animo furandi* to have been equally clear."

By the time I had finished this exordium, Melons had disappeared, as I fully expected.

He never reappeared. The remorse that I have experienced for the part I had taken in what I fear may have resulted in his utter and complete extermination, alas, he may not know, except through these pages. For I have never seen him since. Whether he ran away and went to sea to reappear at some future day as the most ancient of mariners, or whether he buried himself completely in his trousers, I never shall know. I have read the papers anxiously for accounts of him. I have gone to the Police Office in the vain attempt of identifying him as a lost child. But I never saw him or heard of him since. Strange fears have sometimes crossed my mind that his venerable appearance may have been actually the result of senility, and that he may have been gathered peacefully to his fathers in a green old age. I have even had doubts of his existence, and have sometimes thought that he was providentially and mysteriously offered to fill the void I have before alluded to. In that hope I have written these pages.

# THE DEACON'S MASTERPIECE

OR, THE WONDERFUL "ONE-HOSS SHAY"

*A Logical Story*

BY OLIVER WENDELL HOLMES

Have you heard of the wonderful one-hoss shay,
That was built in such a logical way
It ran a hundred years to a day,
And then, of a sudden, it—ah, but stay,
I'll tell you what happened without delay,
Scaring the parson into fits,
Frightening people out of their wits,—
Have you ever heard of that, I say?

Seventeen hundred and fifty-five.
*Georgius Secundus* was then alive,—
Snuffy old drone from the German hive.
That was the year when Lisbon-town
Saw the earth open and gulp her down,
And Braddock's army was done so brown,
Left without a scalp to its crown.
It was on the terrible Earthquake-day
That the Deacon finished the one-hoss shay.

Now in building of chaises, I tell you what,
There is always *somewhere* a weakest spot,—
In hub, tire, felloe, in spring or thill,
In panel, or crossbar, or floor, or sill,

In screw, bolt, thoroughbrace,—lurking still,
Find it somewhere you must and will,—
Above or below, or within or without,—
And that's the reason, beyond a doubt,
That a chaise *breaks down,* but doesn't *wear out.*

But the Deacon swore, (as Deacons do,
With an "I dew vum," or an "I tell *yeou,*")
He would build one shay to beat the taown
'N' the keounty 'n' all the kentry raoun';
It should be so built that it *couldn'* break daown:
—"Fur," said the Deacon, " 't's mighty plain
Thut the weakes' place mus' stan' the strain;
'N' the way t' fix it, uz I maintain,
                    Is only jest
T' make that place uz strong uz the rest."

So the Deacon inquired of the village folk
Where he could find the strongest oak,
That couldn't be split nor bent nor broke,—
That was for spokes and floor and sills;
He sent for lancewood to make the thills;
The crossbars were ash, from the straightest trees,
The panels of whitewood, that cuts like cheese,
But lasts like iron for things like these;
The hubs of logs from the "Settler's ellum,"—
Last of its timber,—they couldn't sell 'em,
Never an axe had seen their chips,
And the wedges flew from between their lips,
Their blunt ends frizzled like celery-tips;
Step and prop-iron, bolt and screw,
Spring, tire, axle, and linchpin too,
Steel of the finest, bright and blue;
Thoroughbrace bison-skin, thick and wide;

Boot, top, dasher, from tough old hide
Found in the pit when the tanner died.
That was the way he "put her through."—
"There!" said the Deacon, "naow she'll dew!"

Do! I tell you, I rather guess
She was a wonder, and nothing less!
Colts grew horses, beards turned gray,
Deacon and deaconess dropped away,
Children and grandchildren—where were they?
But there stood the stout old one-hoss shay
As fresh as on Lisbon-earthquake-day!

EIGHTEEN HUNDRED;—It came and found
The Deacon's masterpiece strong and sound.
Eighteen hundred increased by ten;—
"Hahnsum kerridge" they called it then.
Eighteen hundred and twenty came;—
Running as usual; much the same.
Thirty and forty at last arrive,
And then come fifty, and FIFTY-FIVE.

Little of all we value here
Wakes on the morn of its hundredth year
Without both feeling and looking queer.
In fact, there's nothing that keeps its youth,
So far as I know, but a tree and truth.
(This is a moral that runs at large;
Take it.—You're welcome.—No extra charge.)

FIRST OF NOVEMBER,—The Earthquake-day—
There are traces of age in the one-hoss shay,
A general flavor of mild decay,
But nothing local, as one may say.

There couldn't be,—for the Deacon's art
Had made it so like in every part
That there wasn't a chance for one to start.
For the wheels were just as strong as the thills,
And the floor was just as strong as the sills,
And the panels just as strong as the floor,
And the whipple-tree neither less nor more,
And the back-crossbar as strong as the fore,
And the spring and axle and hub *encore.*
And yet, as a *whole,* it is past a doubt
In another hour it will be *worn out!*

First of November, 'Fifty-five!
This morning the parson takes a drive.
Now, small boys, get out of the way!
Here comes the wonderful one-hoss shay,
Drawn by a rat-tailed, ewe-necked bay.
"Huddup!" said the parson.—Off went they.
The parson was working his Sunday's text,—
Had got to *fifthly,* and stopped perplexed
At what the—Moses—was coming next.
All at once the horse stood still,
Close by the meet'n'-house on the hill.
—First a shiver, and then a thrill,
Then something decidedly like a spill,—
And the parson was sitting upon a rock,
At half past nine by the meet'n'-house clock,—
Just the hour of the Earthquake shock!
—What do you think the parson found,
When he got up and stared around?
The poor old chaise in a heap or mound,
As if it had been to the mill and ground!
You see, of course, if you're not a dunce,
How it went to pieces all at once,—

All at once, and nothing first,—
Just as bubbles do when they burst.

End of the wonderful one-hoss shay.
Logic is logic.   That's all I say.

## THE PURPLE COW

### BY GELETT BURGESS

*Reflections on a Mythic Beast,*
*Who's Quite Remarkable, at Least.*

I never Saw a Purple Cow;
   I never Hope to See One;
But I can Tell you, Anyhow,
   I'd rather See than Be One.

### *Cinq Ans Apres.*

*(Confession: and a Portrait, Too,*
*Upon a Background that I Rue!)*

Ah, yes! I wrote the "Purple Cow"—
   I'm Sorry, now, I Wrote it!
But I can Tell you, Anyhow,
   I'll Kill you if you Quote it!

# THE CURSE OF THE COMPETENT

BY HENRY J. FINN

My spirit hath been seared, as though the lightning's
    scathe had rent,
In the swiftness of its wrath, through the midnight firma-
    ment,
The darkly deepening clouds; and the shadows dim and
    murky
Of destiny are on me, for my dinner's naught but—*turkey*.


The chords upon my silent lute no soft vibrations know,
Save where the moanings of despair—out-breathings of
    my woe—
Tell of the cold and selfish world.   In melancholy mood,
The soul of genius chills with only—*fourteen cords of
    wood*.


The dreams of the deserted float around my curtained
    hours,
And young imaginings are as the thorns bereft of flowers;
A wretched outcast from mankind, my strength of heart
    has sank
Beneath the evils of—*ten thousand dollars in the bank*.


This life to me a desert is, and kindness, as the stream
That singly drops upon the waste where burning breezes
    teem;

A banished, blasted plant, I droop, to which no freshness
     lends
Its healing balm, for Heaven knows, I've but—*a dozen
    friends.*


And Sorrow round my brow has wreathed its coronal of
     thorns;
No dewy pearl of Pleasure my sad sunken eyes adorns;
Calamity has clothed my thoughts, I feel a bliss no
    more,—
Alas! my wardrobe now would only—*stock a clothing
    store.*


The joyousness of Memory from me for aye hath fled;
It dwells within the dreary habitation of the dead;
I breathe my midnight melodies in languor and by stealth,
For Fate inflicts upon my frame—*the luxury of health.*


Envy, Neglect, and Scorn have been my hard inheritance;
And a baneful curse clings to me, like the stain on inno-
    cence;
My moments are as faded leaves, or roses in their
    blight—
I'm asked but once a day to dine—*to parties every night.*


Would that I were a silver ray upon the moonlit air,
Or but one gleam that's glorified by each Peruvian's
    prayer!
My tortured spirit turns from earth, to ease its bitter
    loathing;
My hatred is on all things here, because—*I want for
    nothing.*

# THE GRAMMATICAL BOY

BY BILL NYE

Sometimes a sad, homesick feeling comes over me, when I compare the prevailing style of anecdote and school literature with the old McGuffey brand, so well known thirty years ago. To-day our juvenile literature, it seems to me, is so transparent, so easy to understand, that I am not surprised to learn that the rising generation shows signs of lawlessness.

Boys to-day do not use the respectful language and large, luxuriant words that they did when Mr. McGuffey used to stand around and report their conversations for his justly celebrated school reader. It is disagreeable to think of, but it is none the less true, and for one I think we should face the facts.

I ask the careful student of school literature to compare the following selection, which I have written myself with great care, and arranged with special reference to the matter of choice and difficult words, with the flippant and commonplace terms used in the average school book of to-day.

One day as George Pillgarlic was going to his tasks, and while passing through the wood, he spied a tall man approaching in an opposite direction along the highway.

"Ah!" thought George, in a low, mellow tone of voice, "whom have we here?"

"Good morning, my fine fellow," exclaimed the stranger, pleasantly. "Do you reside in this locality?"

"Indeed I do," retorted George, cheerily, doffing his cap. "In yonder cottage, near the glen, my widowed mother and her thirteen children dwell with me."

"And is your father dead?" exclaimed the man, with a rising inflection.

"Extremely so," murmured the lad, "and, oh, sir, that is why my poor mother is a widow."

"And how did your papa die?" asked the man, as he thoughtfully stood on the other foot a while.

"Alas! sir," said George, as a large hot tear stole down his pale cheek and fell with a loud report on the warty surface of his bare foot, "he was lost at sea in a bitter gale. The good ship foundered two years ago last Christmastide, and father was foundered at the same time. No one knew of the loss of the ship and that the crew was drowned until the next spring, and it was then too late."

"And what is your age, my fine fellow?" quoth the stranger.

"If I live till next October," said the boy, in a declamatory tone of voice suitable for a Second Reader, "I will be seven years of age."

"And who provides for your mother and her large family of children?" queried the man.

"Indeed, I do, sir," replied George, in a shrill tone. "I toil, oh, so hard, sir, for we are very, very poor, and since my elder sister, Ann, was married and brought her husband home to live with us, I have to toil more assiduously than heretofore."

"And by what means do you obtain a livelihood?" exclaimed the man, in slowly measured and grammatical words.

"By digging wells, kind sir," replied George, picking up a tired ant as he spoke and stroking it on the back. "I have a good education, and so I am able to dig wells as

well as a man. I do this day-times and take in washing
at night. In this way I am enabled barely to maintain our
family in a precarious manner; but, oh, sir, should my
other sisters marry, I fear that some of my brothers-in-
law would have to suffer."

"And do you not fear the deadly fire-damp?" asked the
stranger in an earnest tone.

"Not by a damp sight," answered George, with a low
gurgling laugh, for he was a great wag.

"You are indeed a brave lad," exclaimed the stranger,
as he repressed a smile. "And do you not at times become
very weary and wish for other ways of passing your
time?"

"Indeed, I do, sir," said the lad. "I would fain run and
romp and be gay like other boys, but I must engage in
constant manual exercise, or we will have no bread to eat,
and I have not seen a pie since papa perished in the moist
and moaning sea."

"And what if I were to tell you that your papa did not
perish at sea, but was saved from a humid grave?" asked
the stranger in pleasing tones.

"Ah, sir," exclaimed George, in a genteel manner,
again doffing his cap, "I am too polite to tell you what I
would say, and besides, sir, you are much larger than I
am."

"But, my brave lad," said the man in low musical tones,
"do you not know me, Georgie? Oh, George!"

"I must say," replied George, "that you have the advantage of me. Whilst I may have met you before, I can
not at this moment place you, sir."

"My son! oh, my son!" murmured the man, at the same
time taking a large strawberry mark out of his valise and
showing it to the lad. "Do you not recognize your parent
on your father's side? When our good ship went to the

bottom, all perished save me. I swam several miles through the billows, and at last, utterly exhausted, gave up all hope of life. Suddenly I stepped on something hard. It was the United States.

"And now, my brave boy," exclaimed the man with great glee, "see what I have brought for you." It was but the work of a moment to unclasp from a shawl-strap which he held in his hand and present to George's astonished gaze a large forty-cent watermelon, which until now had been concealed by the shawl-strap.

## SIMPLE ENGLISH

### BY RAY CLARKE ROSE

Ofttimes when I put on my gloves,
    I wonder if I'm sane.
For when I put the right one on,
    The right seems to remain
To be put on—that is, 't is left;
    Yet if the left I don,
The other one is left, and then
    I have the right one on.
But still I have the left on right;
    The right one, though, is left
To go right on the left right hand
    All right, if I am deft.

# PARTINGTONIAN PATCHWORK

BY B. P. SHILLABER

## VII

"Are you in favor of the prohibitive law, or the license law?" asked her opposite neighbor of the relict of P. P.; corporal of the "Bloody 'Leventh."

She carefully weighed the question, as though she were selling snuff, and answered,—

"Sometimes I think I am, and then again I think I am not."

Her neighbor was perplexed, and repeated the question, varying it a little.

"Have you seen the 'Mrs. Partington Twilight Soap'?" she asked.

"Yes," was the reply; "everybody has seen that; but why?"

"Because," said the dame, "it has two sides to it, and it is hard to choose between them. Now here are my two neighbors, contagious to me on both sides—one goes for probation, t'other for licentiousness; and I think the best thing for me is to keep nuisance."

She meant neutral, of course. The neighbor admired, and smiled, while Ike lay on the floor, with his legs in the air, trying to balance Mrs. Partington's fancy waiter on his toe.

## IX

Christmas Ike was made the happy possessor of a fiddle, which he found in the morning near his stocking.

"Has he got a musical bent?" Banfield asked, of whom Mrs. Partington was buying the instrument.

"Bent, indeed!" said she; "no, he's as straight as an error."

He explained by repeating the question regarding his musical inclination.

"Yes," she replied; "he's dreadfully inclined to music since he had a drum, and I want the fiddle to see if I can't make another Pickaninny or an Old Bull of him. Jewsharps is simple, though I can't see how King David played on one of 'em, and sung his psalms at the same time; but the fiddle is best, because genius can show itself plainer on it without much noise. Some prefers a violeen; but I don't know."

The fiddle was well improved, till the horsehair all pulled out of the bow, and it was then twisted up into a fish-line.

## XVI

"How limpid you walk!" said a voice behind us, as we were making a hundred and fifty horse-power effort to reach a table whereon reposed a volume of Bacon. "What is the cause of your lameness?" It was Mrs. Partington's voice that spoke, and Mrs. Partington's eyes that met the glance we returned over our left shoulder. "Gout," said we, briefly, almost surlily. "Dear me," said she; "you are highly flavored! It was only rich people and epicacs in living that had the gout in olden times." "Ah!" we growled, partly in response, and partly with an infernal twinge. "Poor soul!" she continued, with commiseration, like an anodyne, in the tones of her voice; "the best remedy I know for it is an embarkation of Roman wormwood and lobelia for the part infected, though some say a cranberry poultice is best; but I believe the cranberries is for erisipilis, and whether either of 'em is a rostrum for the gout or not, I really don't know. If it was a fraction of the arm, I could jest know what to subscribe." We looked into her eye with a determination to say something severely bitter, because we felt allopathic just then; but the kind and sympathizing look that met our own disarmed severity, and sinking into a seat with our coveted Bacon, we thanked her. It was very evident, all the while, that she, or they, stayed, that Ike was seeing how near he could come to our lame member, and not touch it. He did touch it sometimes, but those didn't count.

## XX

"I've always noticed," said Mrs. Partington on New Year's Day, dropping her voice to the key that people adopt when they are disposed to be philosophical or moral; "I've always noticed that every year added to a man's life is apt to make him older, just as a man who goes a journey finds, as he jogs on, that every mile he goes brings him nearer where he is going, and farther from where he started. I am not so young as I was once, and I don't believe I shall ever be, if I live to the age of Samson, which, Heaven knows as well as I do, I don't want to, for I wouldn't be a centurion or an octagon, and survive my factories, and become idiomatic, by any means. But then there is no knowing how a thing will turn out till it takes place; and we shall come to an end some day, though we may never live to see it."

There was a smart tap on the looking-glass that hung upon the wall, followed instantly by another.

"Gracious!" said she; "what's that? I hope the glass isn't fractioned, for it is a sure sign of calamity, and mercy knows they come along full fast enough without helping 'em by breaking looking-glasses."

There was another tap, and she caught sight of a white bean that fell on the floor; and there, reflected in the glass, was the face of Ike, who was blowing beans at the mirror through a crack in the door.

## XXI

"As for the Chinese question," said Mrs. Partington, reflectively, holding her spoon at "present," while the vapor of her cup of tea curled about her face, which shone through it like the moon through a mist, "it is a great pity that somebody don't answer it, though who under the canister of heaven can do it, with sich letters as they have on their tea-chists, is more than I can tell. It is really too bad, though, that some lingister doesn't try it, and not have this provoking question asked all the time, as if we were ignoramuses, and did not know Toolong from No Strong, and there never was sich a thing as the seventh commandment, which, Heaven knows, suits this case to a T, and I hope the breakers of it may escape, but I don't see how they can. The question must be answered, unless it is like a cannondrum, to be given up, which nobody of any spirit should do."

She brought the spoon down into the cup, and looked out through the windows of her soul into celestial fields, peopled with pig-tails, that were all in her eye, while Ike took a double charge of sugar for his tea, and gave an extra allowance of milk to the kitten.

# THE MENAGERIE

BY WILLIAM VAUGHN MOODY

Thank God my brain is not inclined to cut
   Such capers every day! I'm just about
Mellow, but then— There goes the tent flap shut.
   Rain 's in the wind. I thought so : every snout
   Was twitching when the keeper turned me out.

That screaming parrot makes my blood run cold.
   Gabriel's trump! the big bull elephant
Squeals "Rain!" to the parched herd. The monkeys
      scold,
   And jabber that it 's rain-water they want.
   (It makes me sick to see a monkey pant.)

I'll foot it home, to try and make believe
   I'm sober. After this I stick to beer,
And drop the circus when the sane folks leave.
   A man's a fool to look at things too near :
   They look back and begin to cut up queer.

Beasts do, at any rate; especially
   Wild devils caged. They have the coolest way
Of being something else than what you see :
   You pass a sleek young zebra nosing hay,
   A nylghau looking bored and distingué,—

And think you've seen a donkey and a bird.
   Not on your life! Just glance back, if you dare.
The zebra chews, the nylghau has n't stirred;
   But something's happened, Heaven knows what or
      where,
   To freeze your scalp and pompadour your hair.

I'm not precisely an æolian lute
   Hung in the wandering winds of sentiment,
But drown me if the ugliest, meanest brute
   Grunting and fretting in that sultry tent
   Did n't just floor me with embarrassment!

'T was like a thunder-clap from out the clear—
   One minute they were circus beasts, some grand,
Some ugly, some amusing, and some queer:
   Rival attractions to the hobo band,
   The flying jenny, and the peanut-stand.

Next minute they were old hearth-mates of mine!
   Lost people, eyeing me with such a stare!
Patient, satiric, devilish, divine;
   A gaze of hopeless envy, squalid care,
   Hatred, and thwarted love, and dim despair.

Within my blood my ancient kindred spoke—
   Grotesque and monstrous voices, heard afar
Down ocean caves when behemoth awoke,
   Or through fern forests roared the plesiosaur
   Locked with the giant-bat in ghastly war.

And suddenly, as in a flash of light,
   I saw great Nature working out her plan;
Through all her shapes, from mastodon to mite,
   Forever groping, testing, passing on
   To find at last the shape and soul of Man.

Till in the fullness of accomplished time,
   Comes brother Forepaugh, upon business bent,
Tracks her through frozen and through torrid clime,
   And shows us, neatly labeled in a tent,
   The stages of her huge experiment;

Babbling aloud her shy and reticent hours;
   Dragging to light her blinking, slothful moods;
Publishing fretful seasons when her powers
   Worked wild and sullen in her solitudes,
   Or when her mordant laughter shook the woods.

Here, round about me, were her vagrant births;
   Sick dreams she had, fierce projects she essayed;
Her qualms, her fiery prides, her craze mirths;
   The troublings of her spirit as she strayed,
   Cringed, gloated, mocked, was lordly, was afraid,

On that long road she went to seek mankind;
   Here were the darkling coverts that she beat
To find the Hider she was sent to find;
   Here the distracted footprints of her feet
   Whereby her soul's Desire she came to greet.

But why should they, her botch-work, turn about
   And stare disdain at me, her finished job?
Why was the place one vast suspended shout
   Of laughter? Why did all the daylight throb
   With soundless guffaw and dumb-stricken sob?

Helpless I stood among those awful cages;
   The beasts were walking loose, and I was bagged!
I, I, last product of the toiling ages,
   Goal of heroic feet that never lagged—
   A little man in trousers, slightly jagged.

Deliver me from such another jury!
   The Judgment-day will be a picnic to 't.
Their satire was more dreadful than their fury,
   And worst of all was just a kind of brute
   Disgust, and giving up, and sinking mute.

Survival of the fittest adaptation,
   And all their other evolution terms,
Seem to omit one small consideration,
   To wit, that tumblebugs and angleworms
   Have souls: there 's soul in everything that
      squirms.

And souls are restless, plagued, impatient things,
   All dream and unaccountable desire;
Crawling, but pestered with the thought of wings;
   Spreading through every inch of earth's old mire,
   Mystical hanker after something higher.

Wishes *are* horses, as I understand.
   I guess a wistful polyp that has strokes
Of feeling faint to gallivant on land
   Will come to be a scandal to his folk;
   Legs he will sprout, in spite of threats and jokes.

And at the core of every life that crawls
   Or runs or flies or swims or vegetates—
Churning the mammoth's heart-blood, in the galls
   Of shark and tiger planting gorgeous hates,
   Lighting the love of eagles for their mates;

Yes, in the dim brain of the jellied fish
   That is and is not living—moved and stirred
From the beginning a mysterious wish,
   A vision, a command, a fatal Word:
   The name of Man was uttered, and they heard.

Upward along the æons of old war
  They sought him: wing and shank-bone, claw and
      bill,
Were fashioned and rejected; wide and far
  They roamed the twilight jungles of their will;
  But still they sought him, and desired him still.

Man they desired, but mind you, Perfect Man,
  The radiant and the loving, yet to be!
I hardly wonder, when they come to scan
  The upshot of their strenuosity,
  They gazed with mixed emotions upon *me*.

Well, my advice to you is, Face the creatures,
  Or spot them sideways with your weather eye,
Just to keep tab on their expansive features;
  It is n't pleasant when you 're stepping high
  To catch a giraffe smiling on the sly.

If Nature made you graceful, don't get gay
  Back-to before the hippopotamus;
If meek and godly, find some place to play
  Besides right where three mad hyenas fuss;
  You may hear language that we won't discuss.

If you 're a sweet thing in a flower-bed hat,
  Or her best fellow with your tie tucked in,
Don't squander love's bright springtime girding at
  An old chimpanzee with an Irish chin:
  *There may be hidden meaning in his grin.*

# DOWN AROUND THE RIVER

BY JAMES WHITCOMB RILEY

Noon-time and June-time, down around the river!
Have to furse with 'Lizey Ann—but lawzy! I fergive
    her!
Drives me off the place, and says 'at all 'at she's a-wishin',
Land o' gracious! time'll come I'll git enough o' fishin'!
Little Dave, a-choppin' wood, never 'pears to notice;
Don't know where she's hid his hat, er keerin' where his
    coat is,—
Specalatin', more'n like, he haint a-goin' to mind me,
And guessin' where, say twelve o'clock, a feller'd likely
    find me.

Noon-time and June-time, down around the river!
Clean out o' sight o' home, and skulkin' under kivver
Of the sycamores, jack-oaks, and swamp-ash and ellum—
Idies all so jumbled up, you kin hardly tell 'em!—
*Tired,* you know, but *lovin'* it, and smilin' jest to think 'at
Any sweeter tiredness you'd fairly want to *drink* it.
Tired o' fishin'—tired o' fun—line out slack and slacker—
All you want in all the world's a little more tobacker!

Hungry, but *a-hidin'* it, er jes' a-not a-keerin':—
Kingfisher gittin' up and skootin' out o' hearin';
Snipes on the t'other side, where the County Ditch is,
Wadin' up and down the aidge like they'd rolled their
    britches!

Old turkle on the root kindo-sorto drappin'
Intoo th' worter like he don't know how it happen!
Worter, shade and all so mixed, don't know which you'd
    orter
Say, th' *worter* in the shadder—*shadder* in the *worter!*

Somebody hollerin'—'way around the bend in
Upper Fork—where yer eye kin jes' ketch the endin'
Of the shiney wedge o' wake some muss-rat's a-makin'
With that pesky nose o' his! Then a sniff o' bacon,
Corn-bread and 'dock-greens—and little Dave a-shinnin'
'Crost the rocks and mussel-shells, a-limpin' and a-grin-
    nin',
With yer dinner fer ye, and a blessin' from the giver.
Noon-time and June-time down around the river!

# A MEDIEVAL DISCOVERER

BY BILL NYE

Galilei, commonly called Galileo, was born at Pisa on the 14th day of February, 1564. He was the man who discovered some of the fundamental principles governing the movements, habits, and personal peculiarities of the earth. He discovered things with marvelous fluency. Born as he was, at a time when the rotary motion of the earth was still in its infancy and astronomy was taught only in a crude way, Galileo started in to make a few discoveries and advance some theories which he loved.

He was the son of a musician and learned to play several instruments himself, but not in such a way as to arouse the jealousy of the great musicians of his day. They came and heard him play a few selections, and then they went home contented with their own music. Galileo played for several years in a band at Pisa, and people who heard him said that his manner of gazing out over the Pisan hills with a far-away look in his eye after playing a selection, while he gently up-ended his alto horn and worked the mud-valve as he poured out about a pint of moist melody that had accumulated in the flues of the instrument, was simply grand.

At the age of twenty Galileo began to discover. His first discoveries were, of course, clumsy and poorly made, but very soon he commenced to turn out neat and durable discoveries that would stand for years.

It was at this time that he noticed the swinging of a lamp in a church, and, observing that the oscillations were of equal duration, he inferred that this principle might be utilized in the exact measurement of time.

31

From this little accident, years after, came the clock, one of the most useful of man's dumb friends. And yet there are people who will read this little incident and still hesitate about going to church.

Galileo also invented the thermometer, the microscope and the proportional compass. He seemed to invent things not for the money to be obtained in that way, but solely for the joy of being first on the ground. He was a man, of infinite genius and perseverance. He was also very fair in his treatment of other inventors. Though he did not personally invent the rotary motion of the earth, he heartily indorsed it and said it was a good thing. He also came out in a card in which he said that he believed it to be a good thing, and that he hoped some day to see it applied to the other planets.

He was also the inventor of a telescope that had a magnifying power of thirty times. He presented this to the Venetian senate, and it was used in making appropriations for river and harbor improvements.

By telescopic investigation Galileo discovered the presence of microbes in the moon, but was unable to do anything for it. I have spoken of Mr. Galileo, informally calling him by his first name, all the way through this article, for I feel so thoroughly acquainted with him, though there was such a striking difference in our ages, that I think I am justified in using his given name while talking of him.

Galileo also sat up nights and visited with Venus through a long telescope which he had made himself from an old bamboo fishing-rod.

But astronomy is a very enervating branch of science. Galileo frequently came down to breakfast with red, heavy eyes, eyes that were swollen full of unshed tears. Still he persevered. Day after day he worked and toiled.

Year after year he went on with his task till he had worked out in his own mind the satellites of Jupiter and placed a small tin tag on each one, so that he would know it readily when he saw it again. Then he began to look up Saturn's rings and investigate the freckles on the sun. He did not stop at trifles, but went bravely on till everybody came for miles to look at him and get him to write something funny in their autograph albums. It was not an unusual thing for Galileo to get up in the morning, after a wearisome night with a fretful, new-born star, to find his front yard full of albums. Some of them were little red albums with floral decorations on them, while others were the large plush and alligator albums of the affluent. Some were new and had the price-mark still on them, while others were old, foundered albums, with a droop in the back and little flecks of egg and gravy on the title-page. All came with a request for Galileo "to write a little, witty, characteristic sentiment in them."

Galileo was the author of the hydrostatic paradox and other sketches. He was a great reader and a fluent penman. One time he was absent from home, lecturing in Venice for the benefit of the United Aggregation of Mutual Admirers, and did not return for two weeks, so that when he got back he found the front room full of autograph albums. It is said that he then demonstrated his great fluency and readiness as a thinker and writer. He waded through the entire lot in two days with only two men from West Pisa to assist him. Galileo came out of it fresh and youthful, and all of the following night he was closeted with another inventor, a wicker-covered microscope, and a bologna sausage. The investigations were carried on for two weeks, after which Galileo went out to the inebriate asylum and discovered some new styles of reptiles.

Galileo was the author of a little work called "I Discarsi e Dimas-Trazioni Matematiche Intorus a Due Muove Scienze." It was a neat little book, of about the medium height, and sold well on the trains, for the Pisan news-boys on the cars were very affable, as they are now, and when they came and leaned an armful of these books on a passenger's leg and poured into his ear a long tale about the wonderful beauty of the work, and then pulled in the name of the book from the rear of the last car, where it 'had been hanging on behind, the passenger would most always buy it and enough of the name to wrap it up in.

He also discovered the isochronism of the pendulum. He saw that the pendulum at certain seasons of the year looked yellow under the eyes, and that it drooped and did not enter into its work with the old zest. He began to study the case with the aid of his new bamboo telescope and a wicker-covered microscope. As a result, in ten days he had the pendulum on its feet again.

Galileo was inclined to be liberal in his religious views, more especially in the matter of the Scriptures, claiming that there were passages in the Bible which did not liter-ally mean what the translator said they did. This was where Galileo missed it. So long as he discovered stars and isochronisms and such things as that, he succeeded, but when he began to fool with other people's religious beliefs he got into trouble. He was forced to fly from Pisa, we are told by the historian, and we are assured at the same time that Galileo, who had always been far, far ahead of all competitors in other things, was equally suc-cessful as a fleer.

Galileo received but sixty scudi per year as his salary while at Pisa, and a part of that he took in town orders, worth only sixty cents on the scudi.

# WANTED—A COOK

BY ALAN DALE

There was a ring at the front door-bell. Letitia, wrought-up, nervously clutched my arm. For a moment a sort of paralysis seized me. Then, alertly as a young calf, I bounded toward the door, hope aroused, and expectation keen. It was rather dark in the outside hall, and I could not quite perceive the nature of our visitor. But I soon gladly realized that it was something feminine, and as I held the door open, a thin, small, soiled wisp of a woman glided in and smiled at me.

"*Talar ni svensk?*" she asked, but I had no idea what she meant. She may have been impertinent, or even rude, or perhaps improper, but she looked as though she might be a domestic, and I led her gently, reverently, to Letitia in the drawing-room. I smiled back at her, in a wild endeavor to be sympathetic. I would have anointed her, or bathed her feet, or plied her with figs and dates, or have done anything that any nationality craves as a welcome. As the front door closed I heaved a sigh of relief. Here was probably the quintessence of five advertisements. Out of the mountain crept a mouse, and quite a little mouse, too!

"*Talar ni svensk?*" proved to be nothing more outrageous than "Do you speak Swedish?" My astute little wife discovered this intuitively. I left them together, my mental excuse being that women understand each other and that a man is unnecessary, under the circum-

35

stances. I had some misgivings on the subject of Letitia
and *svensk,* but the universal language of femininity is
not without its uses. I devoutly hoped that Letitia would
be able to come to terms, as the mere idea of a cook who
couldn't excoriate us in English was, at that moment,
delightful. At the end of a quarter of an hour I strolled
back to the drawing-room. Letitia was smiling and the
hand-maiden sat grim and uninspired.

"I've engaged her, Archie," said Letitia. "She knows
nothing, as she has told me in the few words of English
that she has picked up, but—you remember what Aunt
Julia said about a clean slate."

I gazed at the maiden, and reflected that while the term
"slate" might be perfectly correct, the adjective seemed
a bit over-enthusiastic. She was decidely soiled, this
quintessence of a quintette of advertisements. I said
nothing, anxious not to dampen Letitia's elation.

"She has no references," continued my wife, "as she
has never been out before. She is just a simple little
Stockholm girl. I like her face immensely, Archie—immensely. She is willing to begin at once, which shows
that she is eager, and consequently likely to suit us. Wait
for me, Archie, while I take her to the kitchen. *Kom,*
Gerda."

Exactly why Letitia couldn't say "Come, Gerda,"
seemed strange. She probably thought that *Kom* must
be Swedish, and that it sounded well. She certainly invented *Kom* on the spur of the Scandinavian moment,
and I learned afterward that it was correct. My inspired
Letitia! Still, in spite of all, my opinion is that "Come,
Gerda," would have done just as well.

"Isn't it delightful?" cried Letitia, when she joined
me later. "I am really enthusiastic at the idea of a
Swedish girl. I adore Scandinavia, Archie. It always

makes me think of Ibsen. Perhaps Gerda Lyberg—that's her name—will be as interesting as Hedda Gabler, and Mrs. Alving, and Nora, and all those lovely complex Ibsen creatures."

"They were Norwegians, dear," I said gently, anxious not to shatter illusions; "the Ibsen plays deal with Christiania, not with Stockholm."

"But they are so near," declared Letitia, amiable and seraphic once more. "Somehow or other, I invariably mix up Norway and Sweden and Denmark. I know I shall always look upon Gerda as an Ibsen girl, who has come here to 'live her life,' or 'work out her inheritance.' Perhaps, dear, she has some interesting internal disease, or a maggoty brain. Don't you think, Archie, that the Ibsen inheritances are always most fascinating? A bit morbid, but surely fascinating."

"I prefer a healthy cook, Letitia," I said meditatively, "somebody willing to interest herself in our inheritance, rather than in her own."

"I don't mind what you say now," she pouted, "I am not to be put down by clamor. We really have a cook at last, and I feel more lenient toward you, Archie. Of course I was only joking when I suggested the Ibsen diseases. Gerda Lyberg may have inherited from her ancestors something quite nice and attractive."

"Then you mustn't look upon her as Ibsen, Letitia," I protested. "The Ibsen people never inherit nice things. Their ancestors always bequeath nasty ones. That is where their consistency comes in. They are receptacles for horrors. Personally, if you'll excuse my flippancy, I prefer Norwegian anchovies to Norwegian heroines. It is a mere matter of opinion."

"I'm ashamed of you," retorted Letitia defiantly. "You talk like some of the wretchedly frivolous criticisms, so called, that men like Acton Davies and Alan Dale inflict upon the long-suffering public. They never amuse me. Ibsen may make his heroines the recipients of ugly legacies, but he has never yet cursed them with the odious incubus known as 'a sense of humor.' The people with a sense of humor have something in their brains worse than maggots. We'll drop the subject, Archie. I'm going to learn Swedish. Before Gerda Lyberg has been with us a month I intend to be able to talk fluently. It will be most useful. Next time we go to Europe we'll take in Sweden, and I'll do the piloting. I am going to buy some Swedish books, and study. Won't it be jolly? And just think how melancholy we were this morning, you and I, looking out of that window, and trying to materialize cooks. Wasn't it funny, Archie? What amusing experiences we shall be able to chronicle, later on!"

Letitia babbled on like half a dozen brooks, and thinking up a gentle parody, in the shape of, "cooks may come, and men may go," I decided to leave my household gods for the bread-earning contest down-town. I could not feel quite as sanguine as Letitia, who seemed to have forgotten the dismal results of the advertisement—just one little puny Swedish result. I should have preferred to make a choice. Letitia was as pleased with Gerda Lyberg as though she had been a selection instead of a that-or-nothing.

If somebody had dramatized Gerda Lyberg's initial dinner, it would probably have been considered exceedingly droll. As a serious episode, however, its humor, to my mind, lacked spontaneity. Letitia had asked her to cook us a little Swedish meal, so that we could get some idea of Stockholm life, in which, for some reason or other, we were supposed to be deeply interested. Unfortunately I was extremely hungry, and had carefully avoided luncheon in order to give my appetite a chance. We sat down to a huge bowl of cold, greasy soup, in which enormous lumps of meat swam, as though for their life, awaiting rescue at the prongs of a fork. In addition to this epicurean dish was a teeming plate of water-soaked potatoes, delicately boiled. That was all. Letitia said that it was Swedish, and the most annoying part of the entertainment was that I was alone in my critical disapprobation. Letitia was so engrossed with a little Swedish conversation book that she brought to table that she forgot the mere material question of food—forgot everything but the horrible jargon she was studying, and the soiled, wisp-like maiden, who looked more unlike a clean slate than ever.

"What shall I say to her, Archie?" asked Letitia, turning over the pages of her book, as I tried to rescue a block of meat from the cold fat in which it lurked. "Here is a chapter on dinner. 'I am very hungry,' *'Jag är myckel hungrig.'* Rather pretty, isn't it? Hark at this: *'Kypare gif mig matsedeln och vinlistan.'* That means: 'Waiter, give me the bill of fare, and the list of wines.'"

"Don't," I cried; "don't. This woman doesn't know what dining means. Look out a chapter on feeding."

Letitia was perfectly unruffled. She paid no attention to me whatsoever. She was fascinated with the slovenly girl, who stood around and gaped at her Swedish.

"Gerda," said Letitia, with her eyes on the book, *"Gif mir apven senap och några potäter."* And then, as Miss Lyberg dived for the drowned potatoes, Letitia exclaimed in an ecstasy of joy, "She understands, Archie, she understands. I feel I am going to be a great success. *Jag tackar,* Gerda. That means 'I thank you,' *Jag tackar.* See if you can say it, Archie. Just try, dear, to oblige me. *Jag tackar.* Now, that's a good boy, *jag tackar."*

39

"I won't," I declared spitefully. "No *jag tackar*ing for a parody like this, Letitia. You don't seem to realize that I'm hungry. Honestly, I prefer a delicatessen dinner to this."

" 'Pray, give me a piece of venison,' " read Letitia, absolutely disregarding my mood. " *'Var god och gif mig ett stycke vildt.'* It is almost intelligible, isn't it, dear? *'Ni äter icke'*: you do not eat."

"I can't," I asserted mournfully, anxious to gain Letitia's sympathy.

It was not forthcoming. Letitia's eyes were fastened on Gerda, and I could not help noting on the woman's face an expression of scorn. I felt certain of it. She appeared to regard my wife as a sort of irresponsible freak, and I was vexed to think that Letitia should make such an exhibition of herself, and countenance the alleged meal that was set before us.

" 'I have really dined very well,' " she continued joyously. *"Jag har verkligen atit mycket bra.' "*

"If you are quite sure that she doesn't understand English, Letitia," I said viciously, "I'll say to you that this is a kind of joke I don't appreciate. I won't keep such a woman in the house. Let us put on our things and go out and have dinner. Better late than never."

Letitia was turning over the pages of her book, quite lost to her surroundings. As I concluded my remarks she looked up and exclaimed, "How very funny, Archie. Just as you said 'Better late than never,' I came across that very phrase in the list of Swedish proverbs. It must be telepathy, dear. 'Better late than never,' *'Battre sent än aldrig.'* What were you saying on the subject, dear? Will you repeat it? And do try it in Swedish. Say *'Battre sent än aldrig.' "*

"Letitia," I shot forth in a fury, "I'm not in the humor

for this sort of thing. I think this dinner and this woman are rotten. See if you can find the word rotten in Swedish."

"I am surprised at you," Letitia declared glacially, roused from her book by my heroic though unparliamentary language. "Your expressions are neither English nor Swedish. Please don't use such gutter-words before a servant, to say nothing of your own wife."

"But she doesn't understand," I protested, glancing at Miss Lyberg. I could have sworn that I detected a gleam in the woman's eyes and that the sphinx-like attitude of dull incomprehensibility suggested a strenuous effort. "She doesn't understand anything. She doesn't want to understand."

"In a week from now," said Letitia, "she will understand everything perfectly, for I shall be able to talk with her. Oh, Archie, do be agreeable. Can't you see that I am having great fun? Don't be such a greedy boy. If you could only enter into the spirit of the thing, you wouldn't be so oppressed by the food question. Oh, dear! How important it does seem to be to men. Gerda, *hur gammal är ni?*"

The maiden sullenly left the room, and I felt convinced that Letitia had Swedishly asked her to do so. I was wrong. "*Hur gammal är ni,*" Letitia explained, simply meant, "How old are you?"

"She evidently didn't want to tell me," was my wife's comment, as we went to the drawing-room. "I imagine, dear, that she doesn't quite like the idea of my ferreting out Swedish so persistently. But I intend to persevere. The worst of conversation books is that one acquires a language in such a parroty way. Now, in my book, the only answer to the question 'How old are you?' is, 'I was born on the tenth of August, 1852.' For the life of me, I couldn't vary that, and it would be most embarrassing. It would make me fifty-two. If any one asked me in Swedish how old I was, I should *have* to be fifty-two!"

"When I think of my five advertisements," I said lugubriously, as I threw myself into an arm-chair, fatigued at my efforts to discover dinner, "when I remember our expectation, and the pleasant anticipations of to-day, I feel very bitter, Letitia. Just to think that from it all nothing has resulted but that beastly mummy, that atrocious ossified thing."

"Archie, Archie!" said my wife warningly; "please be calm. Perhaps I was too engrossed with my studies to note the deficiencies of dinner. But do remember that I pleaded with her for a Swedish meal. The poor thing did what I asked her to do. Our dinner was evidently Swedish. It was not her fault that I asked for it. To-morrow, dear, it shall be different. We had better stick to the American régime. It is more satisfactory to you. At any rate, we have somebody in the house, and if our five advertisements had brought forth five hundred applicants we should only have kept one. So don't torture yourself, Archie. Try and imagine that we *had* five hundred applicants, and that we selected Gerda Lyberg."

"I can't, Letitia," I said sulkily, and I heaved a heavy sigh.

"Come," she said soothingly, "come and study Swedish with me. It will be most useful for your *Lives of Great Men*. You can read up the Swedes in the original. I'll entertain you with this book, and you'll forget all about Mrs. Potz—I mean Gerda Lyberg. By-the-by, Archie, she doesn't remind me so much of Hedda Gabler. I don't fancy that she is very subtile."

"You, Letitia," I retorted, "remind me of Mrs. Nickleby. You ramble on so."

Letitia looked offended. She always declared that Dickens "got on her nerves." She was one of the new-fashioned readers who have learned to despise Dickens. Personally, I regretted only his nauseating sense of humor. Letitia placed a cushion behind my head, smoothed my forehead, kissed me, made her peace, and settled down by my side. Lack of nourishment made me drowsy, and Letitia's babblings sounded vague and muffled.

"It is a most inclusive little book," she said, "and if I can succeed in memorizing it all I shall be quite at home with the language. In fact, dear, I think I shall always keep Swedish cooks. Hark at this: 'If the wind be favorable, we shall be at Gothenburg in forty hours.' *'Om vinden är god, sa äro vi pa pyrtio timmar i Goteborg.'* I think it is sweetly pretty. 'You are seasick.' 'Steward, bring me a glass of brandy and water.' 'We are now entering the harbor.' 'We are now anchoring.' 'Your passports, gentlemen.' "

A comfortable lethargy was stealing o'er me. Letitia took a pencil and paper, and made notes as she plied the book. "A chapter on 'seeing a town' is most interesting, Archie. Of course, it must be a Swedish town. 'Do you know the two private galleries of Mr. Smith, the merchant, and Mr. Muller, the chancellor?' 'To-morrow morning I wish to see all the public buildings and statues.' *'Statyerna'* is Swedish for statues, Archie. Are you listening, dear? 'We will visit the Church of the Holy Ghost, at two, then we will make an excursion on Lake Mälan and see the fortress of Vaxholm.' It *is* a charming little book. Don't you think that it is a great improvement on the old Ollendorff system? I don't find nonsensical sentences like 'The hat of my aunt's sister is blue, but the nose of my brother-in-law's sister-in-law is red.' "

I rose and stretched myself. Letitia was still plunged

in the irritating guide to Sweden, where I vowed I would never go. Nothing on earth should ever induce me to visit Sweden. If it came to a choice between Hoboken and Stockholm, I mentally determined to select the former. As I paced the room I heard a curious splashing noise in the kitchen. Letitia's studies must have dulled her ears. She was evidently too deeply engrossed.

I strolled nonchalantly into the hall, and proceeded deliberately toward the kitchen. The thick carpet deadened my footsteps. The splashing noise grew louder. The kitchen door was closed. I gently opened it. As I did so a wild scream rent the air. There stood Gerda Lyberg in —in—my pen declines to write it—a simple unsophisticated birthday dress, taking an ingenuous reluctant bath in the "stationary tubs," with the plates, and dishes, and dinner things grouped artistically around her!

The instant she saw me she modestly seized a dish-towel and shouted at the top of her voice. The kitchen was filled with the steam from the hot water. 'Venus arising' looked nebulous, and mystic. I beat a hasty retreat, aghast at the revelation, and almost fell against Letitia, who, dropping her conversation book, came to see what had happened.

"She's bathing!" I gasped, "in the kitchen—among the plates—near the soup—"

"Never!" cried Letitia. Then, melodramatically: "Let me pass. Stand aside, Archie. I'll go and see. Perhaps—perhaps—you had better come with me."

"Letitia," I gurgled, "I'm shocked! She has nothing on but a dish-towel."

Letitia paused irresolutely for a second, and going into the kitchen shut the door. The splashing noise ceased. I heard the sound of voices, or rather of a voice—Letitia's! Evidently she had forgotten Swedish, and such remarks as "If the wind be favorable, we shall be at Gothenburg in forty hours." I listened attentively, and could not even hear her say "We will visit the Church of the Holy Ghost at two." It is strange how the stress of circumstances alters the complexion of a conversation book! All the evening she had studied Swedish, and yet suddenly confronted by a Swedish lady bathing in our kitchen, dish-toweled but unashamed, all she could find to say was "How disgusting!" and "How disgraceful!" in English!

"You see," said Letitia, when she emerged, "she is just a simple peasant girl, and only needs to be told. It is very horrid, of course."

"And unappetizing!" I chimed in.

"Of course—certainly unappetizing. I couldn't think of anything Swedish to say, but I said several things in English. She was dreadfully sorry that you had seen her, and never contemplated such a possibility. After all, Archie, bathing is not a crime."

"And we were hunting for a clean slate," I suggested satirically. "Do you think, Letitia, that she also takes a cold bath in the morning, among the bacon and eggs, and things?"

"That is enough," said Letitia sternly. "The episode need not serve as an excuse for indelicacy."

It was with the advent of Gerda Lyberg that we became absolutely certain, beyond the peradventure of any doubt, that there was such a thing as the servant question. The knowledge had been gradually wafted in upon us, but it was not until the lady from Stockholm had definitively planted herself in our midst that we admitted to ourselves openly, unblushingly, that the problem existed. Gerda blazoned forth the enigma in all its force and defiance.

The remarkable thing about our latest acquisition was

the singularly blank state of her gastronomic mind.
There was nothing that she knew. Most women, and a
great many men, intuitively recognize the physical fact
that water, at a ertain temperature, boils. Miss Lyberg,
apparently seeking to earn her living in the kitchen, had
no certain views as to when the boiling point was reached.
Rumors seemed vaguely to have reached her that things
called eggs dropped into water would, in the course of
time—any time, and generally less than a week—become
eatable. Letitia bought a little egg-boiler for her—one
of those antique arrangements in which the sands of time
play to the soft-boiled egg. The maiden promptly boiled
it with the eggs, and undoubtedly thought that the hen,
in a moment of perturbation, or aberration, had laid it.
I say "thought" because it is the only term I can use. It
is, perhaps, inappropriate in connection with Gerda.

Potatoes, subjected to the action of hot water, grow
soft. She was certain of that. Whether she tested them
with the poker, or with her hands or feet, we never knew.
I inclined to the last suggestion. The situation was quite
marvelous. Here was an alleged worker, in a particular
field, asking the wages of skilled labor, and densely ignorant of every detail connected with her task. It seemed
unique. Carpenters, plumbers, bricklayers, seamstresses,
dressmakers, laundresses—all the sowers and reapers in
the little garden of our daily needs, were forced by the
inexorable law of competition to possess some inkling of
the significance of their undertakings. With the cook it
was different. She could step jubilantly into any kitchen
without the slightest idea of what she was expected to do
there. If she knew that water was wet and that fire was
hot, she felt amply primed to demand a salary.

Impelled by her craving for Swedish literature, Letitia struggled with Miss Lyberg. Compared with the

Swede, my exquisitely ignorant wife was a culinary queen. She was an epicurean caterer. Letitia's slate-pencil coffee was ambrosia for the gods, sweetest nectar, by the side of the dishwater that cook prepared. I began to feel quite proud of her. She grew to be an adept in the art of boiling water. If we could have lived on that fluid, everything would have moved clockworkily.

"I've discovered one thing," said Letitia on the evening of the third day. "The girl is just a peasant, probably a worker in the fields. That is why she is so ignorant."

I thought this reasoning foolish. "Even peasants eat, my dear," I muttered. "She must have seen somebody cook something. Field-workers have good appetites. If this woman ever ate, what did she eat and why can't we have the same? We have asked her for no luxuries. We have arrived at the stage, my poor girl, when all we need is, prosaically, to 'fill up.' You have given her opportunities to offer us samples of peasant food. The result has been *nil*."

"It *is* odd," Letitia declared, a wrinkle of perplexity appearing in the smooth surface of her forehead. "Of course, she says she doesn't understand me. And yet, Archie, I have talked to her in pure Swedish."

"I suppose you said, 'Pray give me a piece of venison,' from the conversation book."

"Don't be ridiculous, Archie. I know the Swedish for cauliflower, green peas, spinach, a leg of mutton, mustard, roast meat, soup, and—"

" 'If the wind be favorable, we shall be at Gothenburg in forty hours,' " I interrupted. She was silent, and I went on: "It seems a pity to end your studies in Swedish, Letitia, but fascinating though they be, they do not really necessitate our keeping this barbarian. You can always pursue them, and exercise on me. I don't mind.

Even with an American cook, if such a being exist, you could still continue to ask for venison steak in Swedish, and to look forward to arriving at Gothenburg in forty hours."

Letitia declined to argue. My mood was that known as cranky. We were in the drawing-room, after what we were compelled to call dinner. It had consisted of steak burned to cinders, potatoes soaked to a pulp, and a rice pudding that looked like a poultice the morning after, and possibly tasted like one. Letitia had been shopping, and was therefore unable to supervise. Our delicate repast was capped by "black" coffee of an indefinite straw-color, and with globules of grease on the surface. People who can feel elated with the joy of living, after a dinner of this description, are assuredly both mentally and morally lacking. Men and women there are who will say: "Oh, give me anything. I'm not particular—so long as it is plain and wholesome." I've met many of these people. My experience of them is that they are the greatest gluttons on earth, with veritably voracious appetites, and that the best isn't good enough for them. To be sure, at a pinch, they will demolish a score of potatoes, if there be nothing else; but offer them caviare, canvas-back duck, quail, and nesselrode pudding, and they will look askance at food that is plain and wholesome. The "plain and wholesome" liver is a snare and a delusion, like the "bluff and genial" visitor whose geniality veils all sorts of satire and merciless comment.

Letitia and I both felt weak and miserable. We had made up our minds not to dine out. We were resolved to keep the home up, even if, in return, the home kept us down. Give in, we wouldn't. Our fighting blood was up. We firmly determined not to degenerate into that clammy American institution, the boarding-house feeder and the restaurant diner. We knew the type; in the feminine, it sits at table with its bonnet on, and a sullen gnawing expression of animal hunger; in the masculine, it puts its own knife in the butter, and uses a toothpick. No cook—no lack of cook—should drive us to these abysmal depths.

Letitia made no feint at Ovid. I simply declined to breathe the breath of *The Lives of Great Men.* She read a sweet little classic called "The Table; How to Buy Food, How to Cook It, and How to Serve It," by Alessandro Filippini—a delightful *table-d'hôte*-y name. I lay back in my chair and frowned, waiting until Letitia chose to break the silence. As she was a most chattily inclined person on all occasions, I reasoned that I should not have to wait long. I was right.

"Archie," said she, "according to this book, there is no place in the civilized world that contains so large a number of so-called high-livers as New York City, which was educated by the famous Delmonico and his able lieutenants."

"Great Heaven!" I exclaimed with a groan, "why rub it in, Letitia? I should also say that no city in the world contained so large a number of low-livers."

" 'Westward the course of Empire sways,' " she read, " 'and the great glory of the past has departed from those centers where the culinary art at one time defied all rivals. The scepter of supremacy has passed into the hands of the metropolis of the New World.' "

"What sickening cant!" I cried. "What fiendishly exaggerated restaurant talk! There are perhaps fifty fine restaurants in New York. In Paris there are five hundred finer. Here we have places to eat in; there they have artistic resorts to dine in. One can dine anywhere in Paris. In New York, save for those fifty fine restaurants, one feeds. Don't read any more of your cook-book to me, my girl. It is written to catch the American trade, with the subtile pen of flattery."

"Try and be patriotic, dear," she said soothingly. "Of course, I know you wouldn't allow a Frenchman to say all that, and that you are just talking cussedly with your own wife."

A ring at the bell caused a diversion. We hailed it. We were in the humor to hail anything. The domestic hearth *was* most trying. We were bored to death. I sprang up and ran to the door, a little pastime to which I was growing accustomed. Three tittering young women, each wearing a hat in which roses, violets, poppies, cornflowers, forget-me-nots, feathers and ribbons ran riot, confronted me.

"Miss Gerda Lyberg?" said the foremost, who wore a bright red gown, and from whose hat six spiteful poppies lurched forward and almost hit me in the face.

For a moment, dazed from the cook-book, I was nonplussed. All I could say was "No," meaning that I wasn't Miss Gerda Lyberg. I felt so sure that I wasn't that I was about to close the door.

"She lives here, I believe," asserted the damsel, again shooting forth the poppies.

I came to myself with an effort. "She is the—the cook," I muttered weakly.

"We are her friends," quoth the damsel, an indignant inflection in her voice. "Kindly let us in. We've come to the Thursday sociable."

The three bedizened ladies entered without further parley and went toward the kitchen, instinctively recognizing its direction. I was amazed. I heard a noisy greeting, a peal of laughter, a confusion of tongues, and then— I groped my way back to Letitia.

"They've come to the Thursday sociable!" I cried.

"Who?" she asked in astonishment, and I imparted to her the full extent of my knowledge. Letitia took it very nicely. She had always heard, she said, in fact Mrs. Archer had told her, that Thursday nights were festival occasions with the Swedes. She thought it rather a pleasant and convivial notion. Servants must enjoy themselves, after all. Better a happy gathering of girls than a rowdy collection of men. Letitia thought the idea felicitous. She had no objections to giving privileges to a cook. Nor had I, for the matter of that. I ventured to remark, however, that Gerda didn't seem to be a cook.

"Then let us call her a 'girl,' " said Letitia.

"Gerda is a girl, only because she isn't a boy," I remarked tauntingly. "If by 'girl' you even mean servant, then Gerda isn't a girl. Goodness knows what she is. Hello! Another ring!"

This time Miss Lyberg herself went to the door, and we listened. More arrivals for the sociable; four Swedish guests, all equally gaily attired in flower hats. Some of them wore bangles, the noise of which, in the hall, sounded like an infuriation of sleigh-bells. They were Christina and Sophie and Sadie and Alexandra—as we soon learned. It was wonderful how welcome Gerda made them, and how quickly they were "at home." They rustled through the halls, chatting and laughing and humming. Such merry girls! Such light-hearted little charmers! Letitia stood looking at them through the crack of the drawing-room door. Perhaps it was just as well that somebody should have a good time in our house.

"Just the same, Letitia," I observed, galled, "I think I should say to-morrow that this invasion is most impertinent—most uncalled for."

"Yes, Archie," said Letitia demurely, "you think you should say it. But please don't think *I* shall, for I assure you that I shan't. I suppose that we must discharge her. She can't do anything and she doesn't want to learn. I don't blame her. She can always get the wages she asks, by doing nothing. You would pursue a similar policy, Archie, if it were possible. Everybody would. But all other laborers must know how to labor."

I was glad to hear Letitia echoing my sentiments. She was quite unconsciously plagiarizing. Once again she took up the cook-book. The sound of merrymaking in the kitchen drifted in upon us. From what we could gather, Gerda seemed to be "dressing up" for the delectation of her guests. Shrieks of laughter and clapping of hands made us wince. My nerves were on edge. Had any one at that moment dared to suggest that there was even a suspicion of humor in these proceedings I should have slain him without compunction. Letitia was less irate and tried to comfort me.

Letitia sighed, and shut up the cook-book. Eggs *à la reine* seemed as difficult as trigonometry, or conic sections, or differential calculus—and much more expensive. Certainly the eight giggling cooks in the kitchen, now at the very height of their exhilaration, worried themselves little about such concoctions. My nerves again began to play pranks. The devilish pandemonium infuriated me. Letitia was tired and wanted to go to bed. I was tired and hungry and disillusioned. It was close upon midnight and the Swedish Thursday was about over. I thought it unwise to allow them even an initial minute of Friday. When the clock struck twelve, I marched majestically to the kitchen, threw open the door, revealed the octette in the enjoyment of a mound of ice-cream and a mountain of cake—that in my famished condition made my mouth water—and announced in a severe, yet subdued tone, that the revel must cease.

"You must go at once," I said, "I am going to shut up the house."

Then I withdrew and waited. There was a delay, during which a Babel of tongues was let loose, and then Miss Lyberg's seven guests were heard noisily leaving the house. Two minutes later, there was a knock at our door and Miss Lyberg appeared, her eyes blazing, her face flushed and the expression of the hunted antelope defiantly asserting that it would never be brought to bay, on her perspiring features.

"You've insulted my guests!" she cried, in English as good as my own. "I've had to turn them out of the house, and I've had about enough of this place."

Letitia's face was a psychological study. Amazement, consternation, humiliation—all seemed determined to possess her. Here was the obtuse Swede, for whose dear sake she had dallied with the intricacies of the language of Stockholm, furiously familiar with admirable English! The dense, dumb Scandinavian—the lady of the "me no understand" rejoinder—apparently had the "gift of tongues." Letitia trembled. Rarely have I seen her so thoroughly perturbed. Yet seemingly she was unwilling to credit the testimony of her own ears, for with sudden energy, she confronted Miss Lyberg, and exclaimed imperiously, in Swedish that was either pure or impure: *"Tig. Ga din väg!"*

"Ah, come off!" cried the handmaiden insolently. "I understand English. I haven't been in this country fifteen years for nothing. It's just on account of folks like you that poor hard-working girls, who ain't allowed to take no baths or entertain no lady friends, have to protect themselves. Pretend not to understand them, says I. I've found it worked before this. If they think you don't understand 'em, they'll let you alone and stop worriting.

It's like your impidence to turn my lady-friends out of this flat. It's like your impidence. I'll—"

Letitia's crestfallen look, following upon her perturbation, completely upset me. A wave of indignation swamped me. I advanced, and in another minute Miss Gerda Lyberg would have found herself in the hall, impelled there by a persuasive hand upon her shoulder. However, it was not to be.

"You just lay a hand on me," she said with cold deliberation, and a smile, "and I'll have you arrested for assault. Oh, I know the law. I haven't been in this country fifteen years for nothing. The law looks after poor weak, Swedish girls. Just push me out. It's all I ask. Just you push me out."

She edged up to me defiantly. My blood boiled. I would have mortgaged the prospects of my *Lives of Great Men* (not that they were worth mortgaging) for the exquisite satisfaction of confounding this abominable woman. Then I saw the peril of the situation. I thought of horrid headliners in the papers: "Author charged with abusing servant girl," or, "Arrest of Archibald Fairfax on serious charge," and my mood changed.

"I understood you all the time," continued Miss Lyberg insultingly. "I listened to you. I knew what you thought of me. Now I'm telling you what I think of you. The idea of turning out my lady-friends, on a Thursday night, too! And me a-slaving for them, and a-bathing for them, and a-treating them to ice cream and cake, and in me own kitchen. You ain't no lady. As for you"—I seemed to be her particular pet—"when I sees a man around the house all the time, a-molly-coddling and a-fussing, I says to myself, he ain't much good if he can't trust the women folk alone."

We stood there like dummies, listening to the tirade.

What could we do? To be sure, there were two of us, and we were in our own house. The antagonist, however, was a servant, not in her own house. The situation, for reasons that it is impossible to define, was hers. She knew it, too. We allowed her full sway, because we couldn't help it. The sympathy of the public, in case of violent measures, would not have been on our side. The poor domestic, oppressed and enslaved, would have appealed to any jury of married men, living luxuriously in cheap boarding-houses!

When she left us, as she did when she was completely ready to do so, Letitia began to cry. The sight of her tears unnerved me, and I checked a most unfeeling remark that I intended to make to the effect that, "if the wind be favorable, we shall be at Gothenburg in forty hours."

"It's not that I mind her insolence," she sobbed, "we were going to send her off anyway, weren't we? But it's so humiliating to be 'done.' We've been 'done.' Here have I been working hard at Swedish—writing exercises, learning verbs, studying proverbs—just to talk to a woman who speaks English as well as I do. It's—it's—so —so—mor—mortifying."

"Never mind, dear," I said, drying her eyes for her; "the Swedish will come in handy some day."

"No," she declared vehemently, "don't say that you'll take me to Sweden. I wouldn't go to the hateful country. It's a hideous language, anyway, isn't it, Archie? It is a nasty, laconic, ugly tongue. You heard me say *Tig* to her just now. *Tig* means 'be silent.' Could anything sound more repulsive? *Tig! Tig! Ugh!*"

Letitia stamped her foot. She was exceeding wroth.

# SIMILAR CASES

BY CHARLOTTE PERKINS GILMAN

There was once a little animal,
　　No bigger than a fox,
And on five toes he scampered
　　Over Tertiary rocks.
They called him Eohippus,
　　And they called him very small,
And they thought him of no value—
　　When they thought of him at all;
For the lumpish old Dinoceras
　　And Coryphodon so slow
Were the heavy aristocracy
　　In days of long ago.

Said the little Eohippus,
　　"I am going to be a horse!
And on my middle finger-nails
　　To run my earthly course!
I'm going to have a flowing tail!
　　I'm going to have a mane!
I'm going to stand fourteen hands high
　　On the psychozoic plain!"

The Coryphodon was horrified,
　　The Dinoceras was shocked;
And they chased young Eohippus,
　　But he skipped away and mocked;

Then they laughed enormous laughter,
   And they groaned enormous groans,
And they bade young Eohippus
   Go view his father's bones:
Said they, "You always were as small
   And mean as now we see,
And that's conclusive evidence
   That you're always going to be:
What! Be a great, tall, handsome beast,
   With hoofs to gallop on?
*Why, you'd have to change your nature!*"
   Said the Loxolophodon:
They considered him disposed of,
   And retired with gait serene;
That was the way they argued
   In "the early Eocene."


There was once an Anthropoidal Ape,
   Far smarter than the rest,
And everything that they could do
   He always did the best;
So they naturally disliked him,
   And they gave him shoulders cool,
And when they had to mention him
   They said he was a fool.


Cried this pretentious Ape one day,
   "I'm going to be a Man!
And stand upright, and hunt, and fight,
   And conquer all I can!
I'm going to cut down forest trees,
   To make my houses higher!
I'm going to kill the Mastodon!
   I'm going to make a fire!"

Loud screamed the Anthropoidal Apes,
   With laughter wild and gay;
They tried to catch that boastful one,
   But he always got away;
So they yelled at him in chorus,
   Which he minded not a whit;
And they pelted him with cocoanuts,
   Which didn't seem to hit;
And then they gave him reasons,
   Which they thought of much avail,
To prove how his preposterous
   Attempt was sure to fail.

Said the sages, "In the first place,
   The thing can not be done!
And, second, if it *could* be,
   It would not be any fun!
And, third, and most conclusive
   And admitting no reply,
*You would have to change your nature!*
   We should like to see you try!"
They chuckled then triumphantly,
   These lean and hairy shapes,
For these things passed as arguments
   With the Anthropoidal Apes.

There was once a Neolithic Man,
   An enterprising wight,
Who made his chopping implements
   Unusually bright;
Unusually clever he,
   Unusually brave,
And he drew delightful Mammoths
   On the borders of his cave.

To his Neolithic neighbors,
　　Who were startled and surprised,
Said he, "My friends, in course of time,
　　We shall be civilized!
We are going to live in cities!
　　We are going to fight in wars!
We are going to eat three times a day
　　Without the natural cause!
We are going to turn life upside down
　　About a thing called gold!
We are going to want the earth, and take
　　As much as we can hold!
We are going to wear great piles of stuff
　　Outside our proper skins!
We are going to have Diseases!
　　And Accomplishments!! And Sins!!!

Then they all rose up in fury
　　Against their boastful friend,
For prehistoric patience
　　Cometh quickly to an end:
Said one, "This is chimerical!
　　Utopian! Absurd!"
Said another, "What a stupid life!
　　Too dull, upon my word!"
Cried all, "Before such things can come,
　　You idiotic child,
*You must alter Human Nature!*"
　　And they all sat back and smiled:
Thought they, "An answer to that last
　　It will be hard to find!"
It was a clinching argument
　　To the Neolithic Mind!

# THE OLD MAID'S HOUSE: IN PLAN

## BY ELIZABETH STUART PHELPS

Corona had five hundred dollars and some pluck for her enterprise. She had also at her command a trifle for furnishing. But that seemed very small capital. Her friends at large discouraged her generously. Even Tom said he didn't know about that, and offered her three hundred more.

This manly offer she declined in a womanly manner.

"It is to be *my* house, thank you, Tom, dear. I can live in yours at home." . . .

Corona's architectural library was small. She found on the top shelf one book on the construction of chicken-roosts, a pamphlet in explanation of the kindergarten system, a cook-book that had belonged to her grand-mother, and a treatise on crochet. There her domestic literature came to an end. She accordingly bought a book entitled "North American Homes"; then, having, in addition, begged or borrowed everything within two covers relating to architecture that was to be found in her immediate circle of acquaintance, she plunged into that unfamiliar science with hopeful zeal.

The result of her studies was a mixed one. It was necessary, it seemed, to construct the North American home in so many contradictory methods, or else fail forever of life, liberty, and the pursuit of happiness, that Corona felt herself to be laboring under a chronic aberration of mind. . . . Then the plans. Well, the plans, it must be confessed, Corona *did* find it difficult to understand. She always had found it difficult to understand such things; but then she had hoped several weeks of close architectural study would shed light upon the density of the subject. She grew quite morbid about it. She counted the steps when she went up-stairs to bed at night. She estimated the bedroom post when she walked in the cold, gray dawn. . . . .

But the most perplexing thing about the plans was how one story ever got upon another. Corona's imagination never fully grappled with this fact, although her intellect accepted it. She took her books down-stairs one night, and Susy came and looked them over.

"Why, these houses are all one-story," said Susy. "Besides, they 're nothing but lines, anyway. I should n't draw a house so."

Corona laughed with some embarrassment and no effort at enlightenment. She was not used to finding herself and Susy so nearly on the same intellectual level as in this instance. She merely asked: "How should you draw it?"

"Why, so," said Susy, after some severe thought. So she took her little blunt lead pencil, that the baby had chewed, and drew her plan as follows:

SUSY'S PLAN

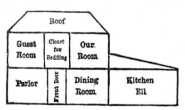

Nursery and your room behind.

Corona made no comment upon this plan, except to ask Susy if that were the way to spell L; and then to look in the dictionary, and find that it was not spelled at all. Tom came in, and asked to see what they were doing.

"I'm helping Corona," said Susy, with much complacency. "These architects' things don't look any more like houses than they do like the first proposition in Euclid; and the poor girl is puzzled."

"*I'll* help you to-morrow, Co," said Tom, who was in too much of a hurry to glance at his wife's plan. But to-morrow Tom went into town by the early train, and when Corona emerged from her "North American Homes," with wild eye and knotted brow, at 5 o'clock P. M., she found Susy crying over a telegram which ran:

Called to California immediately. Those lost cargoes A No. 1 hides turned up. Can't get home to say good-by. Send overcoat and flannels by Simpson on midnight express. Gone four weeks. Love to all.          Tom.

This unexpected event threw Corona entirely upon her own resources; and, after a few days more of patient research, she put on her hat, and stole away at dusk to a builder she knew of down-town—a nice, fatherly man who had once built a piazza for Tom and had just been elected superintendent of the Sunday-school. These combined facts gave Corona confidence to trust her case to his hands. She carried a neat little plan of her own with her, the result of several days' hard labor. Susy's plan she had taken the precaution to cut into paper dolls for the baby. Corona found the good man at home, and in her most business-like manner presented her points.

"Got any plan in yer own head?" asked the builder, hearing her in silence. In silence Corona laid before him the paper which had cost her so much toil.

It was headed in her clear black hand:

## PLAN

### FOR A SMALL BUT HAPPY

## HOME

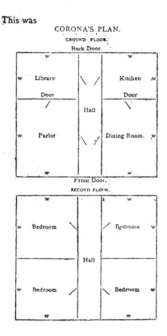

This was

CORONA'S PLAN.

"Well," said the builder, after a silence,—"well, I've seen worse."

"Thank you," said Corona, faintly.

"How does she set?" asked the builder.

"Who set?" said Corona, a little wildly. She could think of nothing that set but hens.

"Why, the house. Where's the points o' compass?"

"I hadn't thought of those," said Corona.

"And the chimney," suggested the builder. "Where's your chimneys?"

"I didn't put in any chimneys," said Corona.

"Where did you count on your stairs?" pursued the builder.

"Stairs? I—forgot the stairs."

"That's natural," said Mr. Timbers. "Had a plan brought me once without an entry or a window to it. It wasn't a woman did it, neither. It was a widower, in the noospaper line. What's your scale?"

"Scale?" asked Corona, without animation.

"Scale of feet. Proportions."

"Oh! I didn't have any scales, but I thought about forty feet front would do. I have but five hundred dollars. A small house must answer."

The builder smiled. He said he would show her some plans. He took a book from his table and opened at a plate representing a small, snug cottage, not uncomely. It stood in a flourishing apple-orchard, and a much larger house appeared dimly in the distance, upon a hill. The The cottage was what is called a "story-and-half" and contained six rooms. The plan was drawn with the beauty of science.

"There," said Mr. Timbers, "I know a lady built one of those upon her brother-in-law's land. He give her the land, and she just put up the cottage, and they was all as pleasant as pease about it. That's about what I'd recommend to you, if you don't object to the name of it."

"What is the matter with the name?" asked Corona.

"Why," said the builder, hesitating, "it is called the Old Maid's House—in the *book*."

"Mr. Timbers," said Corona, with decision, "why should we seek further than the truth? I will have that house. Pray, draw me the plan at once."

# DISTICHS

BY JOHN HAY

## I

Wisely a woman prefers to a lover a man who neglects
her.
This one may love her some day, some day the lover will
not.

## II

There are three species of creatures who when they seem
coming are going,
When they seem going they come: Diplomates, women,
and crabs.

## III

Pleasures too hastily tasted grow sweeter in fond recollection,
As the pomegranate plucked green ripens far over the
sea.

## IV

As the meek beasts in the Garden came flocking for Adam
to name them,
Men for a title to-day crawl to the feet of a king.

### V

What is a first love worth, except to prepare for a second?
What does the second love bring? Only regret for the
first.

### VI

Health was wooed by the Romans in groves of the laurel
and myrtle.
Happy and long are the lives brightened by glory and
love.

### VII

Wine is like rain: when it falls on the mire it but makes
it the fouler,
But when it strikes the good soil wakes it to beauty and
bloom.

### VIII

Break not the rose; its fragrance and beauty are surely
sufficient:
Resting contented with these, never a thorn shall you feel.

### IX

When you break up housekeeping, you learn the extent
of your treasures;
Till he begins to reform, no one can number his sins.

### X

Maidens! why should you worry in choosing whom you
shall marry?
Choose whom you may, you will find you have got somebody else.

## XI

Unto each man comes a day when his favorite sins all for-
 sake him,
And he complacently thinks he has forsaken his sins.

## XII

Be not too anxious to gain your next-door neighbor's approval:
Live your own life, and let him strive your approval to
 gain.

## XIII

Who would succeed in the world should be wise in the
 use of his pronouns.
Utter the You twenty times, where you once utter the I.

## XIV

The best-loved man or maid in the town would perish
 with anguish
Could they hear all that their friends say in the course of
 a day.

## XV

True luck consists not in holding the best of the cards at
 the table:
Luckiest he who knows just when to rise and go home.

## XVI

Pleasant enough it is to hear the world speak of your vir-
 tues;
But in your secret heart 'tis of your faults you are proud.

## XVII

Try not to beat back the current, yet be not drowned in
    its waters;
Speak with the speech of the world, think with the
    thoughts of the few.

## XVIII

Make all good men your well-wishers, and then, in the
    years' steady sifting,
Some of them turn into friends. Friends are the sunshine
    of life.

## THE QUARREL

BY S. E. KISER

"There are quite as good fish
    In the sea
      As any one ever has caught,"
    Said he.
"But few of the fish—
    In the sea
      Will bite at such bait as you've got,"
    Said she.
To-day he is gray, and his line's put away,
    But he often looks back with regret;
She's still "in the sea," and how happy
    she'd be
If he were a fisherman yet!

# A LETTER FROM MR. BIGGS

BY E. W. HOWE

MY DEAR SIR—Occasionally a gem occurs to me which I am unable to favor you with because of late we are not much together. Appreciating the keen delight with which you have been kind enough to receive my philosophy, I take the liberty of sending herewith a number of ideas which may please and benefit you, and which I have divided into paragraphs with headings.

### HAPPINESS

I have observed that happiness and brains seldom go together. The pin-headed woman who regards her thin-witted husband as the greatest man in the world, is happy, and much good may it do her. In such cases ignorance is a positive blessing, for good sense would cause the woman to realize her distressed condition. A man who can think he is as "good as anybody" is happy. The fact may be notorious that the man is not so "good as anybody" until he is as industrious, as educated, and as refined as anybody, but he has not brains enough to know this, and, content with conceit, is happy. A man with a brain large enough to understand mankind is always wretched and ashamed of himself.

### REPUTATION

Reputation is not always desirable. The only thing I

have ever heard said in Twin Mounds concerning Smoky Hill is that good hired girls may be had there.

### WOMEN

1. Most women seem to love for no other reason than that it is expected of them.

2. I know too much about women to honor them more than they deserve; in fact I know all about them. I visited a place once where doctors are made, and saw them cut up one.

3. A woman loses her power when she allows a man to find out all there is to her; I mean by this that familiarity breeds contempt. I knew a young man once who worked beside a woman in an office, and he never married.

4. If men would only tell what they actually know about women, instead of what they believe or hear, they would receive more credit for chastity than is now the case, for they deserve more.

### LACK OF SELF-CONFIDENCE

As a people we lack self-confidence. The country is full of men that will readily talk you to death privately, who would run away in alarm if asked to preside at a public meeting. In my Alliance movement I often have trouble in getting out a crowd, every farmer in the neighborhood feeling of so much importance as to fear that if he attends he will be called upon to say something.

### IN DISPUTE

In some communities where I have lived the women were mean to their husbands; in others, the husbands were mean to their wives. It is usually the case that the friends of a wife believe her husband to be a brute, and the friends of the husband believe the wife to possess no other talent than to make him miserable. You can't tell how it is; the evidence is divided.

### MAN

There is only one grade of men; they are all contemptible. The judge may seem to be a superior creature so long as he keeps at a distance, for I have never known one who was not constantly trying to look wise and grave; but when you know him, you find there is nothing remarkable about him except a plug hat, a respectable coat, and a great deal of vanity, induced by the servility of those who expect favors.

### OPPORTUNITY

You hear a great many persons regretting lack of opportunity. If every man had opportunity for his desires, this would be a nation of murderers and disgraced women.

### EXPECTATION

Always be ready for that which you do not expect. Nothing that you expect ever happens. You have perhaps observed that when you are waiting for a visitor at the front door, he comes in at the back, and surprises you.

### WOMAN'S WORK

A woman's work is never done, as the almanacs state, for the reason that she does not go about it in time to finish it.

### THE GREATEST OF THESE IS CHARITY

If you can not resist the low impulse to talk about people, say only what you actually know, instead of what you have heard. And, while you are about it, stop and consider whether you are not in need of charity yourself.

### NEIGHBORS

Every man overestimates his neighbors, because he does not know them so well as he knows himself. A sensible man despises himself because he knows what a contemptible creature he is. I despise Lytle Biggs, but I happen to know that his neighbors are just as bad.

### VIRTUE

Men are virtuous because the women are; women are virtuous from necessity.

### ASHAMED OF THE TRUTH

I believe I never knew any one who was not ashamed of the truth. Did you ever notice that a railroad company numbers its cars from 1,000, instead of from 1?

### KNOWING ONLY ONE OF THEM

We are sometimes unable to understand why a pretty little woman marries a fellow we know to be worthless; but the fellow, who knows the woman better than we do, considers that he has thrown himself away. We know the fellow, but we do not know the woman.

### AN APOLOGY

I detest an apology. The world is full of people who are always making trouble and apologizing for it. If a man respects me, he will not give himself occasion for apology. An offense can not be wiped out in that way. If it could, we would substitute apologies for hangings. I hope you will never apologize to me; I should regard it as evidence that you had wronged me.

### OLDEST INHABITANTS

The people of Smoky Hill are only fit for oldest inhabitants. In thirty or forty years from now there will be a great demand for reminiscences of the pioneer days. I recommend that they preserve extensive data for the only period in their lives when they can hope to attract attention.

Be good enough, sir, to regard me, as of old, your friend. L. BIGGS.

*To* NED WESTLOCK, *Twin Mounds.*

# MRS. JOHNSON

BY WILLIAM DEAN HOWELLS

It was on a morning of the lovely New England May that we left the horse-car, and, spreading our umbrellas, walked down the street to our new home in Charlesbridge, through a storm of snow and rain so finely blent by the influences of this fortunate climate, that no flake knew itself from its sister drop, or could be better identified by the people against whom they beat in unison. A vernal gale from the east fanned our cheeks and pierced our marrow and chilled our blood, while the raw, cold green of the adventurous grass on the borders of the sopping side-walks gave, as it peered through its veil of melting snow and freezing rain, a peculiar cheerfulness to the landscape. Here and there in the vacant lots abandoned hoop-skirts defied decay; and near the half-finished wooden houses, empty mortar-beds, and bits of lath and slate strewn over the scarred and mutilated ground, added their interest to the scene. . . .

This heavenly weather, which the Pilgrim Fathers, with the idea of turning their thoughts effectually from earthly pleasures, came so far to discover, continued with slight amelioration throughout the month of May and far into June; and it was a matter of constant amazement with one who had known less austere climates, to behold how vegetable life struggled with the hostile skies, and, in an atmosphere as chill and damp as that of a cellar, shot forth the buds and blossoms upon the pear-trees, called out the sour Puritan courage of the currant-bushes, taught a reckless native grape-vine to wander and wanton over the southern side of the fence, and decked the banks with violets as fearless and as fragile as New England girls; so that about the end of June, when the heavens relented and the sun blazed out at last, there was little for him to do but to redden and darken the daring fruits that had attained almost their full growth without his countenance.

Then, indeed, Charlesbridge appeared to us a kind of Paradise. The wind blew all day from the southwest, and all day in the grove across the way the orioles sang to their nestlings. . . . The house was almost new and in perfect repair; and, better than all, the kitchen had as yet given no signs of unrest in those volcanic agencies which are constantly at work there, and which, with sudden explosions, make Herculaneums and Pompeiis of so many smiling households. Breakfast, dinner, and tea came up with illusive regularity, and were all the most perfect of their kind; and we laughed and feasted in our vain security. We had out from the city to banquet with us the friends we loved, and we were inexpressibly proud before them of the Help, who first wrought miracles of cookery in our honor, and then appeared in a clean white apron, and the glossiest black hair, to wait upon the table. She was young, and certainly very pretty; she was as gay as a lark, and was courted by a young man whose clothes would have been a credit, if they had not been a reproach, to our lowly basement. She joyfully assented to the idea of staying with us till she married.

In fact, there was much that was extremely pleasant about the little place when the warm weather came, and it was not wonderful to us that Jenny was willing to remain. It was very quiet; we called one another to the window if a large dog went by our door; and whole days passed without the movement of any wheels but the butcher's upon our street, which flourished in ragweed and buttercups and daisies, and in the autumn burned, like the borders of nearly all the streets in Charlesbridge, with the pallid azure flame of the succory. The neighborhood was in all things a frontier between city and country. The horse-cars, the type of such civilization—full of imposture, discomfort, and sublime possibility—as we yet possess, went by the head of our street, and might, perhaps, be available to one skilled in calculating the movements of comets; while two minutes' walk would take us into a wood so wild and thick that no roof was visible through the trees. We learned, like innocent pastoral people of the golden age, to know the several voices of the cows pastured in the vacant lots, and, like engine-drivers of the iron age, to distinguish the different whistles of the locomotives passing on the neighboring railroad. . . .

We played a little at gardening, of course, and planted tomatoes, which the chickens seemed to like, for they ate them up as fast as they ripened; and we watched with pride the growth of our Lawton blackberries, which, after attaining the most stalwart proportions, were still as bitter as the scrubbiest of their savage brethren, and which, when by advice left on the vines for a week after they turned black, were silently gorged by secret and gluttonous flocks of robins and orioles. As for our grapes, the frost cut them off in the hour of their triumph.

So, as I have hinted, we were not surprised that Jenny should be willing to remain with us, and were as little prepared for her desertion as for any other change of our mortal state. But one day in September she came to her nominal mistress with tears in her beautiful eyes and protestations of unexampled devotion upon her tongue, and said that she was afraid she must leave us. She liked the place, and she never had worked for any one that was more of a lady, but she had made up her mind to go into the city. All this, so far, was quite in the manner of domestics who, in ghost stories, give warning to the occupants of haunted houses; and Jenny's mistress listened in suspense for the motive of her desertion, expecting to hear no less than that it was something which walked up and down the stairs and dragged iron links after it, or something that came and groaned at the front door, like populace dissatisfied with a political candidate. But it was in fact nothing of this kind; simply, there were no lamps upon our street, and Jenny, after spending Sunday evening with friends in East Charlesbridge, was always alarmed, on her return, in walking from the horse-car to our door. The case was hopeless, and Jenny and our household parted with respect and regret.

We had not before this thought it a grave disadvantage that our street was unlighted. Our street was not drained nor graded; no municipal cart ever came to carry away our ashes; there was not a water-butt within half a mile to save us from fire, nor more than the one-thousandth part of a policeman to protect us from theft. Yet, as I paid a heavy tax, I somehow felt that we enjoyed the benefits of city government, and never looked upon Charlesbridge as in any way undesirable for residence. But when it became necessary to find help in Jenny's place, the frosty welcome given to application at the intelligence offices renewed a painful doubt awakened by her departure. To be sure, the heads of the offices were polite enough; but when the young housekeeper had stated her case at the first to which she applied, and the

Intelligencer had called out to the invisible expectants in the adjoining room, "Anny wan wants to do giner'l housewark in Charlsbrudge?" there came from the maids invoked so loud, so fierce, so full a "No!" as shook the lady's heart with an indescribable shame and dread. The name that, with an innocent pride in its literary and historical associations, she had written at the heads of her letters, was suddenly become a matter of reproach to her; and she was almost tempted to conceal thereafter that she lived in Charlesbridge, and to pretend that she dwelt upon some wretched little street in Boston. "You see," said the head of the office, "the gairls doesn't like to live so far away from the city. Now, if it was on'y in the Port." . . .

This pen is not graphic enough to give the remote reader an idea of the affront offered to an inhabitant of Old Charlesbridge in these closing words. Neither am I of sufficiently tragic mood to report here all the sufferings undergone by an unhappy family in finding servants, or to tell how the winter was passed with miserable makeshifts. Alas! is it not the history of a thousand experiences? Any one who looks upon this page could match it with a tale as full of heartbreak and disaster, while I conceive that, in hastening to speak of Mrs. Johnson, I approach a subject of unique interest. . . .

I say, our last Irish girl went with the last snow, and on one of those midsummer-like days that sometimes fall in early April to our yet bleak and desolate zone, our hearts sang of Africa and golden joys. A Libyan longing took us, and we would have chosen, if we could, to bear a strand of grotesque beads, or a handful of brazen gauds, and traffic them for some sable maid with crisp locks, whom, uncoffling from the captive train beside the desert, we should make to do our general housework forever, through the right of lawful purchase. But we knew that this was impossible, and that, if we desired colored help, we must seek it at the intelligence office, which is in one of those streets chiefly inhabited by the orphaned children and grandchildren of slavery. To tell the truth these orphans do not seem to grieve much for their bereavement, but lead a life of joyous, and rather indolent oblivion in their quarter of the city. They are often to be seen sauntering up and down the street by which the Charlesbridge cars arrive,—the young with a harmless swagger, and the old with the generic limp which our Autocrat has already noted as attending advanced years in their race. . . . How gayly are the young ladies of this race attired, as they trip up and down the sidewalks, and in and out through the pendent garments at the shop-doors! They are the black pansies and marigolds and dark-blooded dahlias among womankind. They try to assume something of our colder race's demeanor, but even the passer on the horse-car can see that it is not native with them, and is better pleased when they forget us, and ungenteelly laugh in encountering friends, letting their white teeth glitter through the generous lips that open to their ears. In the streets branching upward from this avenue, very little colored men and maids play with broken or enfeebled toys, or sport on the wooden pavements of the entrances to the inner courts. Now and then a colored soldier or sailor—looking strange in his uniform, even after the custom of several years—emerges from those passages; or, more rarely, a black gentleman, stricken in years, and cased in shining broadcloth, walks solidly down the brick sidewalk, cane in hand,—a vision of serene self-complacency, and so plainly the expression of virtuous public sentiment that the great colored louts, innocent enough till then in their idleness, are taken with a sudden sense of depravity, and loaf guiltily up against the house-walls. At the same moment, perhaps, a young damsel, amorously scuffling with an admirer through one of the low open windows, suspends the strife, and bids him,—"Go along now, do!" More rarely yet than the gentleman described, one may see a white girl among the dark neighbors, whose frowsy head is uncovered, and whose sleeves are rolled up to her elbows, and who, though no doubt quite at home, looks as strange there as that pale anomaly which may sometimes be seen among a crew of blackbirds.

An air not so much of decay as of unthrift, and yet hardly of unthrift, seems to prevail in the neighborhood, which has none of the aggressive and impudent squalor of an Irish quarter, and none of the surly wickedness of a low American street. A gayety not born of the things that bring its serious joy to the true New England heart —a ragged gayety, which comes of summer in the blood, and not in the pocket or the conscience, and which affects the countenance and the whole demeanor, setting the feet to some inward music, and at times bursting into a line of song or a child-like and irresponsible laugh—gives tone to the visible life, and wakens a very friendly spirit in the passer, who somehow thinks there of a milder climate, and is half persuaded that the orange-peel on the sidewalks came from fruit grown in the soft atmosphere of those back courts.

It was in this quarter, then, that we heard of Mrs. Johnson; and it was from a colored boarding-house there that she came out to Charlesbridge to look at us, bringing her daughter of twelve years with her. She was a matron of mature age and portly figure, with a complexion like coffee soothed with the richest cream; and her manners were so full of a certain tranquillity and grace, that she charmed away all our will to ask for references. It was only her barbaric laughter and lawless eye that betrayed how slightly her New England birth and breeding covered her ancestral traits, and bridged the gulf of a thousand years of civilization that lay between her race and ours. But in fact, she was doubly estranged by descent; for, as we learned later, a sylvan wildness mixed with that of the desert in her veins: her grandfather was an Indian, and her ancestors on this side had probably sold their lands for the same value in trinkets that bought the original African pair on the other side.

The first day that Mrs. Johnson descended into our kitchen, she conjured from the malicious disorder in which it had been left by the flitting Irish kobold a dinner that revealed the inspirations of genius, and was quite different from a dinner of mere routine and laborious talent. Something original and authentic mingled with the accustomed flavors; and, though vague reminiscences of canal-boat travel and woodland camps arose from the relish of certain of the dishes, there was yet the assurance of such power in the preparation of the whole, that we knew her to be merely running over the chords of our appetite with preliminary savors, as a musician acquaints his touch with the keys of an unfamiliar piano before breaking into brilliant and triumphant execution. Within a week she had mastered her instrument; and thereafter there was no faltering in her performances, which she varied constantly, through inspiration or from suggestion. . . . But, after all, it was in puddings that Mrs. Johnson chiefly excelled. She was one of those cooks—rare as men of genius in literature—who love their own dishes; and she had, in her personally child-like simplicity of taste, and the inherited appetites of her savage forefathers, a dominant passion for sweets. So far as we could learn, she subsisted principally upon puddings and tea. Through the same primitive instincts, no doubt, she loved praise. She openly exulted in our artless flatteries of her skill; she waited jealously at the head of the kitchen stairs to hear what was said of her work, especially if there were guests; and she was never too weary to attempt emprises of cookery.

While engaged in these, she wore a species of sightly handkerchief like a turban upon her head, and about her person those mystical swathings in which old ladies of the African race delight. But she most pleasured our sense of beauty and moral fitness when, after the last pan was washed and the last pot was scraped, she lighted a potent pipe, and, taking her stand at the kitchen door, laded the soft evening air with its pungent odors. If we surprised her at these supreme moments, she took the pipe from her lips, and put it behind her, with a low, mellow chuckle, and a look of half-defiant consciousness; never guessing that none of her merits took us half so much as the cheerful vice which she only feigned to conceal.

Some things she could not do so perfectly as cooking because of her failing eyesight, and we persuaded her that spectacles would both become and befriend a lady of her years, and so bought her a pair of steel-bowed glasses. She wore them in some great emergencies at first, but had clearly no pride in them. Before long she laid them aside altogether, and they had passed from our thoughts, when one day we heard her mellow note of laughter and her daughter's harsher cackle outside our door, and, opening it, beheld Mrs. Johnson in gold-bowed spectacles of massive frame. We then learned that their purchase was in fulfilment of a vow made long ago, in the life-time of Mr. Johnson, that, if ever she wore glasses, they should be gold-bowed; and I hope the manes of the dead were half as happy in these votive spectacles as the simple soul that offered them.

She and her late partner were the parents of eleven children, some of whom were dead, and some of whom were wanderers in unknown parts. During his life-time she had kept a little shop in her native town; and it was only within a few years that she had gone into service. She cherished a natural haughtiness of spirit, and resented control, although disposed to do all she could of her own notion. Being told to say when she wanted an afternoon, she explained that when she wanted an afternoon she always took it without asking, but always planned so as not to discommode the ladies with whom she lived. These, she said, had numbered twenty-seven within three years, which made us doubt the success of her system in all cases, though she merely held out the fact as an assurance of her faith in the future, and a proof of the ease with which places are to be found. She contended, moreover, that a lady who had for thirty years had a house of her own, was in nowise bound to ask permission to receive visits from friends where she might be living, but that they ought freely to come and go like other guests. In this spirit she once invited her son-in-law, Professor Jones of Providence, to dine with her; and her defied mistress, on entering the dining-room, found the Professor at pudding and tea there,—an impressively respectable figure in black clothes, with a black face rendered yet more effective by a pair of green goggles. It appeared that this dark professor was a light of phrenology in Rhode Island, and that he was believed to have uncommon virtue in his science by reason of being blind as well as black.

I am loath to confess that Mrs. Johnson had not a flattering opinion of the Caucasian race in all respects. In fact, she had very good philosophical and Scriptural reasons for looking upon us as an upstart people of new blood, who had come into their whiteness by no creditable or pleasant process. The late Mr. Johnson, who had died in the West Indies, whither he voyaged for his health in quality of cook upon a Down-East schooner, was a man of letters, and had written a book to show the superiority of the black over the white branches of the human family. In this he held that, as all islands have been at their discovery found peopled by blacks, we must needs believe that humanity was first created of that color. Mrs. Johnson could not show us her husband's work (a sole copy in the library of an English gentleman at Port au Prince is not to be bought for money), but she often developed its arguments to the lady of the house; and one day, with a great show of reluctance, and many protests that no personal slight was meant, let fall the fact that Mr. Johnson believed the white race descended from Gehaz, the leper, upon whom the leprosy of Naaman fell when the latter returned by Divine favor to his original blackness. "And he went out from his presence a leper as white as snow," said Mrs. Johnson, quoting irrefutable Scripture. "Leprosy, leprosy," she added thoughtfully,— "nothing but leprosy bleached you out."

It seems to me much in her praise that she did not exult in our taint and degradation, as some white philosophers used to do in the opposite idea that a part of the human family were cursed to lasting blackness and slavery in Ham and his children, but even told us of a remarkable approach to whiteness in many of her own offspring. In a kindred spirit of charity, no doubt, she refused ever to attend church with people of her elder and wholesomer blood. When she went to church, she said, she always went to a white church, though while with us I am bound to say she never went to any. She professed to read her

Bible in her bedroom on Sundays; but we suspected, from certain sounds and odors which used to steal out of this sanctuary, that her piety more commonly found expression in dozing and smoking.

I would not make a wanton jest here of Mrs. Johnson's anxiety to claim honor for the African color, while denying this color in many of her own family. It afforded a glimpse of the pain which all her people must endure, however proudly they hide it or light-heartedly forget it, from the despite and contumely to which they are guiltlessly born; and when I thought how irreparable was this disgrace and calamity of a black skin, and how irreparable it must be for ages yet, in this world where every other shame and all manner of wilful guilt and wickedness may hope for covert and pardon, I had little heart to laugh. Indeed, it was so pathetic to hear this poor old soul talk of her dead and lost ones, and try, in spite of all Mr. Johnson's theories and her own arrogant generalizations, to establish their whiteness, that we must have been very cruel and silly people to turn her sacred fables even into matter of question. I have no doubt that her Antoinette Anastasia and her Thomas Jefferson Wilberforce —it is impossible to give a full idea of the splendor and scope of the baptismal names in Mrs. Johnson's family— have as light skins and as golden hair in heaven as her reverend maternal fancy painted for them in our world. There, certainly, they would not be subject to tanning, which had ruined the delicate complexion, and had knotted into black woolly tangles the once wavy blonde locks of our little maid-servant Naomi; and I would fain believe that Toussaint Washington Johnson, who ran away to sea so many years ago, has found some fortunate zone where his hair and skin keep the same sunny and rosy tints they wore to his mother's eyes in infancy. But

I have no means of knowing this, or of telling whether he was the prodigy of intellect that he was declared to be. Naomi could no more be taken in proof of the one assertion than of the other. When she came to us, it was agreed that she should go to school; but she overruled her mother in this as in everything else, and never went. Except Sunday-school lessons, she had no other instruction than that her mistress gave her in the evenings, when a heavy day's play and the natural influences of the hour conspired with original causes to render her powerless before words of one syllable.

The first week of her services she was obedient and faithful to her duties; but, relaxing in the atmosphere of a house which seems to demoralize all menials, she shortly fell into disorderly ways of lying in wait for callers out of doors, and, when people rang, of running up the front steps, and letting them in from the outside. As the season expanded, and the fine weather became confirmed, she modified even this form of service, and spent her time in the fields, appearing at the house only when nature importunately craved molasses. . . .

In her untamable disobedience, Naomi alone betrayed her sylvan blood, for she was in all other respects negro and not Indian. But it was of her aboriginal ancestry that Mrs. Johnson chiefly boasted,—when not engaged in argument to maintain the superiority of the African race. She loved to descant upon it as the cause and explanation of her own arrogant habit of feeling; and she seemed indeed to have inherited something of the Indian's hauteur along with the Ethiop's supple cunning and abundant amiability. She gave many instances in which her pride had met and overcome the insolence of employers, and the kindly old creature was by no means singular in her pride of being reputed proud.

She could never have been a woman of strong logical faculties, but she had in some things a very surprising and awful astuteness. She seldom introduced any purpose directly, but bore all about it, and then suddenly sprung it upon her unprepared antagonist. At other times she obscurely hinted a reason, and left a conclusion to be inferred; as when she warded off reproach for some delinquency by saying in a general way that she had lived with ladies who used to come scolding into the kitchen after they had taken their bitters. "Quality ladies took their bitters regular," she added, to remove any sting of personality from her remark; for, from many things she had let fall, we knew that she did not regard us as quality. On the contrary, she often tried to overbear us with the gentility of her former places; and would tell the lady over whom she reigned, that she had lived with folks worth their three and four hundred thousand dollars, who never complained as she did of the ironing. Yet she had a sufficient regard for the literary occupations of the family, Mr. Johnson having been an author. She even professed to have herself written a book, which was still in manuscript, and preserved somewhere among her best clothes.

It was well, on many accounts, to be in contact with a mind so original and suggestive as Mrs. Johnson's. We loved to trace its intricate yet often transparent operations, and were perhaps too fond of explaining its peculiarities by facts of ancestry,—of finding hints of the Powwow or the Grand Custom in each grotesque development. We were conscious of something warmer in this old soul than in ourselves, and something wilder, and we chose to think it the tropic and the untracked forest. She had scarcely any being apart from her affection; she had no morality, but was good because she neither hated nor

87

envied; and she might have been a saint far more easily than far more civilized people.

There was that also in her sinuous yet malleable nature, so full of guile and so full of goodness, that reminded us pleasantly of lowly folks in elder lands, where relaxing oppressions have lifted the restraints of fear between master and servant, without disturbing the familiarity of their relation. She advised freely with us upon all household matters, and took a motherly interest in whatever concerned us. She could be flattered or caressed into almost any service, but no threat or command could move her. When she erred she never acknowledged her wrong in words, but handsomely expressed her regrets in a pudding, or sent up her apologies in a favorite dish secretly prepared. We grew so well used to this form of exculpation, that, whenever Mrs. Johnson took an afternoon at an inconvenient season, we knew that for a week afterwards we should be feasted like princes. She owned frankly that she loved us, that she never had done half so much for people before, and that she never had been nearly so well suited in any other place; and for a brief and happy time we thought that we never should part.

One day, however, our dividing destiny appeared in the basement, and was presented to us as Hippolyto Thucydides, the son of Mrs. Johnson, who had just arrived on a visit to his mother from the State of New Hampshire. He was a heavy and loutish youth, standing upon the borders of boyhood, and looking forward to the future with a vacant and listless eye. I mean this was his figurative attitude; his actual manner, as he lolled upon a chair beside the kitchen window, was so eccentric that we felt a little uncertain how to regard him, and Mrs. Johnson openly described him as peculiar. He was so deeply tanned by the fervid suns of the New Hampshire winter, and his hair had so far suffered from the example of the sheep lately under his charge, that he could not be classed by any stretch of comparison with the blonde and straight-haired members of Mrs. Johnson's family.

He remained with us all the first day until late in the afternoon, when his mother took him out to get him a boarding-house. Then he departed in the van of her and Naomi, pausing at the gate to collect his spirits, and, after he had sufficiently animated himself by clapping his palms together, starting off down the street at a hand-gallop, to the manifest terror of the cows in the pasture, and the confusion of the less demonstrative people of our household. Other characteristic traits appeared in Hippolyto Thucydides within no very long period of time, and he ran away from his lodgings so often during the summer that he might be said to board round among the out-lying cornfields and turnip-patches of Charlesbridge. As a check upon this habit, Mrs. Johnson seemed to have invited him to spend his whole time in our basement; for whenever we went below we found him there, balanced—perhaps in homage to us, and perhaps as a token of extreme sensibility in himself—upon the low window-sill, the bottoms of his boots touching the floor inside, and his face buried in the grass without.

We could formulate no very tenable objection to all this, and yet the presence of Thucydides in our kitchen unaccountably oppressed our imaginations. We beheld him all over the house, a monstrous eidolon, balanced upon every window-sill; and he certainly attracted un-pleasant notice to our place, no less by his furtive and hangdog manner of arrival than by the bold displays with which he celebrated his departures. We hinted this to Mrs. Johnson, but she could not enter into our feeling.

Indeed, all the wild poetry of her maternal and primitive nature seemed to cast itself about this hapless boy; and if we had listened to her we should have believed there was no one so agreeable in society, or so quick-witted in affairs, as Hippolyto, when he chose. . . .

At last, when we said positively that Thucydides should come to us no more, and then qualified the prohibition by allowing him to come every Sunday, she answered that she never would hurt the child's feelings by telling him not to come where his mother was; that people who did not love her children did not love her; and that, if Hippy went, she went. We thought it a masterstroke of firmness to rejoin that Hippolyto must go in any event; but I am bound to own that he did not go, and that his mother stayed, and so fed us with every cunning propitiatory dainty, that we must have been Pagans to renew our threat. In fact, we begged Mrs. Johnson to go into the country with us, and she, after long reluctation on Hippy's account, consented, agreeing to send him away to friends during her absence.

We made every preparation, and on the eve of our departure Mrs. Johnson went into the city to engage her son's passage to Bangor, while we awaited her return in untroubled security.

But she did not appear till midnight, and then responded with but a sad "Well, sah!" to the cheerful "Well, Mrs. Johnson!" that greeted her.

"All right, Mrs. Johnson?"

Mrs. Johnson made a strange noise, half chuckle and half death-rattle, in her throat. "All wrong, sah. Hippy's off again; and I've been all over the city after him."

"Then you can't go with us in the morning?"

"How *can* I, sah?"

Mrs. Johnson went sadly out of the room. Then she

came back to the door again, and opening it, uttered, for the first time in our service, words of apology and regret: "I hope I ha'n't put you out any. I *wanted* to go with you, but I ought to *knowed* I could n't. All is, I loved you too much."

## PASS

### BY IRONQUILL

A father said unto his hopeful son,
"Who was Leonidas, my cherished one?"
The boy replied, with words of ardent nature,
"He was a member of the legislature."
"How?" asked the parent; then the youngster saith:
"He got a pass, and held her like grim death."
"Whose pass? what pass?" the anxious father cried;
" 'T was the'r monopoly," the boy replied.

In deference to the public, we must state,
That boy has been an orphan since that date.

## TEACHING BY EXAMPLE

### BY JOHN G. SAXE

"What is the 'Poet's License,' say?"
    Asked rose-lipped Anna of a poet.
"Now give me an example, pray,
    That when I see one I may know it."
Quick as a flash he plants a kiss
    Where perfect kisses always fall.
"Nay, sir! what liberty is this?"
    "The *Poet's License,*—that is all!"

# WHEN ALBANI SANG*

BY WILLIAM HENRY DRUMMOND

Was workin' away on de farm dere, wan morning not
    long ago,
Feexin' de fence for winter—'cos dat's w'ere we got de
    snow!
W'en Jeremie Plouffe, ma neighbor, come over an' spik
    wit' me,
"Antoine, you will come on de city, for hear Ma-dam
    All-ba-nee?"

"W'at you mean?" I was sayin' right off, me, "Some
    woman was mak' de speech,
Or girl on de Hooraw Circus, doin' high kick an'
    screech?"
"Non—non," he is spikin'—"Excuse me, dat's be Ma-
    dam All-ba-nee
Was leevin' down here on de contree, two mile 'noder side
    Chambly.

"She's jus' comin' over from Englan', on steamboat ar-
    rive Kebeck,
Singin' on Lunnon an' Paree, an' havin' beeg tam, I ex-
    pec',
But no matter de moche she enjoy it, for travel all roun'
    de worl',
Somet'ing on de heart bring her back here, for she was de
    Chambly girl.

*From "The Habitant and Other French Canadian Poems," by
William Henry Drummond. Copyright 1897 by G. P. Putnam's Sons.

"She never do not'ing but singin' an' makin' de beeg
  grande tour
An' travel on summer an' winter, so mus' be de firs' class
  for sure!
Ev'ryboddy I'm t'inkin' was know her, an' I also hear
  'noder t'ing,
She's frien' on La Reine Victoria an' show her de way to
  sing!"

"Wall," I say, "you're sure she is Chambly, w'at you call
  Ma-dam All-ba-nee?
Don't know me dat nam' on de Canton—I hope you're not
  fool wit' me?"
An he say, "Lajeunesse, dey was call her, before she is
  come mariée,
But she's takin' de nam' of her husban'—I s'pose dat's de
  only way."

"C'est bon, mon ami," I was say me, "If I get t'roo de
  fence nex' day
An' she don't want too moche on de monee, den mebbe I
  see her play."
So I finish dat job on to-morrow, Jeremie he was helpin'
  me too,
An' I say, "Len' me t'ree dollar quickly for mak' de voyage wit' you."

Correc'—so we're startin' nex' morning, an' arrive Mon-
  treal all right,
Buy dollar tiquette on de bureau, an' pass on de hall dat
  night.
Beeg crowd, wall! I bet you was dere too, all dress on
  some fancy dress,
De lady, I don't say not'ing, but man's all w'ite shirt an'
  no ves'.

Don't matter, w'en ban' dey be ready, de foreman strek
    out wit' hees steek,
An' fiddle an' ev'ryt'ing else too, begin for play up de
    musique.
It's fonny t'ing too dey was playin' don't lak it mese'f
    at all,
I rader be lissen some jeeg, me, or w'at you call "Affer
    de ball."

An' I'm not feelin' very surprise den, w'en de crowd holler
    out, "Encore,"
For mak' all dem feller commencin' an' try leetle piece
    some more,
'Twas better wan' too, I be t'inkin', but slow lak you're
    goin' to die,
All de sam', noboddy say not'ing, dat mean dey was
    satisfy.

Affer dat come de Grande piano, lak we got on Chambly
    Hotel,
She's nice lookin' girl was play dat, so of course she's go
    off purty well,
Den feller he's ronne out an' sing some, it's all about very
    fine moon,
Dat shine on Canal, ev'ry night too, I'm sorry I don't
    know de tune.

Nex' t'ing I commence get excite, me, for I don't see no
    great Ma-dam yet,
Too bad I was los all dat monee, an' too late for de raffle
    tiquette!
W'en jus' as I feel very sorry, for come all de way from
    Chambly,
Jeremie he was w'isper, "Tiens, tiens, prenez garde, she's
    comin' Ma-dam All-ba-nee!"

Ev'ryboddy seem glad w'en dey see her, come walkin'
    right down de platform,
An' way dey mak' noise on de han' den, w'y! it's jus' lak
    de beeg tonder storm!
I'll never see not'ing lak dat, me, no matter I travel de
    worl',
An' Ma-dam, you t'ink it was scare her? Non, she laugh
    lak de Chambly girl!

Dere was young feller comin' behin' her, walk nice,
    comme un Cavalier,
An' before All-ba-nee she is ready an' piano get startin'
    for play,
De feller commence wit' hees singin', more stronger dan
    all de res',
I t'ink he's got very bad manner, know not'ing at all
    politesse.

Ma-dam, I s'pose she get mad den, an' before anyboddy
    can spik,
She settle right down for mak' sing too, an' purty soon
    ketch heem up quick,
Den she's kip it on gainin' an' gainin', till de song it is
    tout finis,
An' w'en she is beatin' dat feller, Bagosh! I am proud
    Chambly!

I'm not very sorry at all, me, w'en de feller was ronnin'
    away,
An' man he's come out wit' de piccolo, an' start heem
    right off for play,
For it's kin' de musique I be fancy, Jeremie he is lak it
    also,
An' wan de bes' t'ing on dat ev'ning is man wit' de pic-
    colo!

Den mebbe ten minute is passin', Ma-dam she is comin'
    encore,
Dis tam all alone on de platform, dat feller don't show up
    no more,
An' w'en she start off on de singin' Jeremie say, "Antoine,
    dat's Français,"
Dis give us more pleasure, I tole you, 'cos w'y? We're de
    pure Canayen!


Dat song I will never forget me, 't was song of de leetle
    bird,
W'en he's fly from it's nes' on de tree top, 'fore res' of de
    worl' get stirred,
Ma-dam she was tole us about it, den start off so quiet an'
    low,
An' sing lak de bird on de morning, de poor leetle small
    oiseau.


I 'member wan tam I be sleepin' jus' onder some beeg pine
    tree
An song of de robin wak' me, but robin he don't see me,
Dere's not'ing for scarin' dat bird dere, he's feel all alone
    on de worl',
Wall! Ma-dam she mus' lissen lak dat too, w'en she was
    de Chambly girl!


Cos how could she sing dat nice chanson, de sam' as de
    bird I was hear,
Till I see it de maple an' pine tree an' Richelieu ronnin'
    near,
Again I'm de leetle feller, lak young colt upon de spring
Dat's jus' on de way I was feel, me, w'en Ma-dam All-ba-
    nee is sing!

An' affer de song it is finish, an' crowd is mak' noise **wit'**
    its han',
I s'pose dey be t'inkin' I'm crazy, dat mebbe I don't on-
    derstan',
Cos I'm set on de chair very quiet, mese'f an' poor Jere-
    mie,
An' I see dat hees eye it was cry too, jus' sam' way it go
    wit' me.

Dere's rosebush outside on our garden, ev'ry spring it has
    got new nes',
But only wan bluebird is buil' dere, I know her from all
    de res',
An' no matter de far she be flyin' away on de winter tam,
Back to her own leetle rosebush she's comin' dere jus' de
    sam'.

We're not de beeg place on our Canton, mebbe cole on de
    winter, too,
But de heart's "Canayen" on our body an' dat's warm
    enough for true!
An' w'en All-ba-nee was got lonesome for travel all roun'
    de worl'
I hope she'll come home, lak de bluebird, an' again be de
    Chambly girl!

# COLONEL STERETT'S PANTHER HUNT

BY ALFRED HENRY LEWIS

"Panthers, what we-all calls 'mountain lions,'" observed the Old Cattleman, wearing meanwhile the sapient air of him who feels equipped of his subject, "is plenty furtive, not to say mighty sedyoolous to skulk. That's why a gent don't meet up with more of 'em while pirootin' about in the hills. Them cats hears him, or they sees him, an' him still ignorant tharof; an' with that they bashfully withdraws. Which it's to be urged in favor of mountain lions that they never forces themse'fs on no gent; they're shore considerate, that a-way, an' speshul of themse'fs. If one's ever hurt, you can bet it won't be a accident. However, it ain't for me to go 'round impugnin' the motives of no mountain lion; partic'lar when the entire tribe is strangers to me complete. But still a love of trooth compels me to concede that if mountain lions ain't cowardly, they're shore cautious a lot. Cattle an' calves they passes up as too bellicose, an' none of 'em ever faces any anamile more warlike than a baby colt or mebby a half-grown deer. I'm ridin' along the Caliente once when I hears a crashin' in the bushes on the bluff above—two hundred foot high, she is, an' as sheer as the walls of this yere tavern. As I lifts my eyes, a fear-frenzied mare an' colt comes chargin' up an' projects themse'fs over the precipice an' lands in the valley below. They're dead as Joolius Cæsar when I rides onto 'em, while a brace of mountain lions is skirtin' up an' down the aige of the bluff they leaps from, mewin' an' lashin' their long tails in hot enthoosiasm. Shore, the cats has been chasin' the mare an' foal, an' they locoes 'em to that extent they don't know where they're headin' an' makes the death jump I relates. I bangs away with my six-shooter, but beyond givin' the mountain lions a convulsive start I can't say I does any execootion. They turns an' goes streakin' it through the pine woods like a drunkard to a barn raisin'.

"Timid? Shore! They're that timid, seminary girls compared to 'em is as sternly courageous as a passel of buccaneers. Out in Mitchell's canyon a couple of the Lee-Scott riders cuts the trail of a mountain lion and her two kittens. Now whatever do you-all reckon this old tabby does? Basely deserts her offsprings without even barin' a tooth, an' the cow-punchers takes 'em gently by their tails an' beats out their joovenile brains. That's straight; that mother lion goes swarmin' up the canyon like she ain't got a minute to live. An' you can gamble the limit that where a anamile sees its children perish without frontin' up for war, it don't possess the commonest roodiments of sand. Sech, son, is mountain lions.

"It's one evenin' in the Red Light when Colonel Sterett, who's got through his day's toil on that *Coyote* paper he's editor of, onfolds concernin' a panther round-up which he pulls off in his yooth.

"'This panther hunt,' says Colonel Sterett, as he fills his third tumbler, 'occurs when mighty likely I'm goin' on seventeen winters. I'm a leader among my young companions at the time; in fact, I allers is. An' I'm proud to say that my soopremacy that a-way is doo to the dom'-nant character of my intellects. I'm ever bright an' sparklin' as a child, an' I recalls how my aptitoode for

99

learnin' promotes me to be regyarded as the smartest lad
in my set. If thar's visitors to the school, or if the
selectman invades that academy to sort o' size us up, the
teacher allers plays me on 'em. I'd go to the front for the
outfit. Which I'm wont on sech harrowin' o'casions to
recite a ode—the teacher's done wrote it himse'f—an'
which is entitled *Napoleon's Mad Career*. Thar's twenty-
four stanzas to it; an' while these interlopin' selectmen
sets thar lookin' owley an' sagacious, I'd wallop loose
with the twenty-four verses, stampin' up and down, an'
accompanyin' said recitations with sech a multitood of
reckless gestures, it comes plenty clost to backin' everybody plumb outen the room. Yere's the first verse:

> I'd drink an' sw'ar an' r'ar an' t'ar
> An' fall down in the mud,
> While the y'earth for forty miles about
> Is kivered with my blood.

" 'You-all can see from that speciment that our school-
master ain't simply flirtin' with the muses when he origi-
nates that epic; no, sir, he means business; an' whenever
I throws it into the selectmen, I does it jestice. The trus-
tees used to silently line out for home when I finishes, an'
never a yeep. It stuns 'em; it shore fills 'em to the brim!

" 'As I gazes r'arward,' goes on the Colonel, as by one
rapt impulse he uplifts both his eyes an' his nosepaint, 'as
I gazes r'arward, I says, on them sun-filled days, an'
speshul if ever I gets betrayed into talkin' about 'em, I
can hardly t'ar myse'f from the subject. I explains yere-
tofore, that not only by inclination but by birth, I'm a
shore-enough 'ristocrat. This captaincy of local fashion
I assoomes at a tender age. I wears the record as the first
child to don shoes throughout the entire summer in that
neighborhood; an' many a time an' oft does my yoothful

but envy-eaten compeers lambaste me for the insultin' in-
novation. But I sticks to my moccasins; an' to-day shoes
in the Bloo Grass is almost as yooniversal as the licker
habit.

" 'Thar dawns a hour, however, when my p'sition in the
van of Kaintucky *ton* comes within a ace of bein' ser'ously
shook. It's on my way to school one dewy mornin' when
I gets involved all inadvertent in a onhappy rupture with
a polecat. I never does know how the misonderstandin'
starts. After all, the seeds of said dispoote is by no means
important; it's enough to say that polecat finally has me
thoroughly convinced.

" 'Followin' the difference an' my defeat, I'm witless
enough to keep goin' on to school, whereas I should have
returned homeward an' cast myse'f upon my parents as a
sacred trust. Of course, when I'm in school I don't go
impartin' my troubles to the other chil'en; I emyoolates
the heroism of the Spartan boy who stands to be eat by a
fox, an' keeps 'em to myself. But the views of my late
enemy is not to be smothered; they appeals to my young
companions; who tharupon puts up a most onneedful riot
of coughin's an' sneezin's. But nobody knows me as the
party who's so pungent.

" 'It's a tryin' moment. I can see that, once I'm lo-
cated, I'm goin' to be as onpop'lar as a b'ar in a hawg pen;
I'll come tumblin' from my pinnacle in that proud com-
moonity as the glass of fashion an' the mold of form.
You can go your bottom *peso,* the thought causes me to
feel plenty perturbed.

" 'At this peril I has a inspiration; as good, too, as I
ever entertains without the aid of rum. I determines to
cast the opprobrium on some other boy an' send the hunt
of gen'ral indignation sweepin' along his trail.

" 'Thar's a innocent infant who's a stoodent at this

temple of childish learnin' an' his name is Riley Bark. This Riley is one of them giant children who's only twelve an' weighs three hundred pounds. An' in proportions as Riley is a son of Anak, physical, he's dwarfed mental; he ain't half as well upholstered with brains as a shepherd dog. That's right; Riley's intellects, is like a fly in a saucer of syrup, they struggles 'round plumb slow. I decides to uplift Riley to the public eye as the felon who's disturbin' that seminary's sereneity. Comin' to this decision, I p'ints at him where he's planted four seats ahead, all tangled up in a spellin' book, an' says in a loud whisper to a child who's sittin' next:

" ' "Throw him out!"'

" 'That's enough. No gent will ever realize how easy it is to direct a people's sentiment ontil he take a whirl at the game. In two minutes by the teacher's bull's-eye copper watch, every soul knows it's pore Riley; an' in three, the teacher's done drug Riley out doors by the ha'r of his head an' chased him home. Gents, I look back on that yoothful feat as a triumph of diplomacy; it shore saved my standin' as the Beau Brummel of the Bloo Grass

" 'Good old days, them!' observes the Colonel mournfully, 'an' ones never to come ag'in! My sternest studies is romances, an' the peroosals of old tales as I tells you-all prior fills me full of moss an' mockin' birds in equal parts. I reads deep of *Walter Scott* an' waxes to be a sharp on Moslems speshul. I dreams of the Siege of Acre, an' Richard the Lion Heart; an' I simply can't sleep nights for honin' to hold a tournament an' joust a whole lot for some fair lady's love.

" 'Once I commits the error of my career by joustin' with my brother Jeff. This yere Jeff is settin' on the bank of the Branch fishin' for bullpouts at the time, an' Jeff don't know I'm hoverin' near at all. Jeff's reedic'lous fond

of fishin'; which he'd sooner fish than read *Paradise Lost.*
I'm romancin' along, sim'larly bent, when I notes Jeff
perched on the bank. To my boyish imagination Jeff at
once turns to be a Paynim. I drops my bait box, couches
my fishpole, an' emittin' a impromptoo warcry, charges
him. It's the work of a moment; Jeff's onhossed an' falls
into the Branch.

" 'But thar's bitterness to follow vict'ry. Jeff emerges
like Diana from the bath an' frales the wamus off me with
a club. Talk of puttin' a crimp in folks! Gents, when
Jeff's wrath is assuaged I'm all on one side like the lean-
in' tower of Pisa. Jeff actooally confers a skew-gee to
my spinal column.

" 'A week later my folks takes me to a doctor. That
practitioner puts on his specs an' looks me over with
jealous care.

" ' "Whatever's wrong with him, Doc?" says my
father.

" ' "Nothin'," says the physician, "only your son
Willyum's five inches out o' plumb."

" 'Then he rigs a contraption made up of guy-ropes
an' stay-laths, an' I has to wear it; an' mebby in three or
four weeks or so he's got me warped back into the per-
pendic'lar.'

" 'But how about this cat hunt?' asks Dan Boggs.
'Which I don't aim to be introosive none, but I'm camped
yere through the second drink waitin' for it, an' these pro-
crastinations is makn' me kind o' batty.'

" 'That panther hunt is like this,' says the Colonel,
turnin' to Dan. 'At the age of seventeen, me an' eight or
nine of my intimate brave comrades founds what we-all
denom'nates as the "Chevy Chase Huntin' Club." Each
of us maintains a passel of odds an' ends of dogs, an' at
stated intervals we convenes on hosses, an' with these

103

fourscore curs at our tails goes yellin' an' skally-hootin'
up an' down the countryside allowin' we're shore a band
of Nimrods.

" 'The Chevy Chasers ain't been in bein' as a institoo-
tion over long when chance opens a gate to ser'ous work.
The deep snows in the Eastern mountains it looks like
has done drove a panther into our neighborhood. You
could hear of him on all sides. Folks glimpses him now
an' then. They allows he's about the size of a yearlin'
calf; an' the way he pulls down sech feeble people as
sheep or lays desolate some he'pless henroost don't bother
him a bit. This panther spreads a horror over the county.
Dances, pra'er meetin's, an' even poker parties is broken
up, an' the social life of that region begins to bog down.
Even a weddin' suffers; the bridesmaids stayin' away lest
this ferocious monster should show up in the road an'
chaw one of 'em while she's *en route* for the scene of
trouble. That's gospel trooth! the pore deserted bride
has to heel an' handle herse'f an' never a friend to yoonite
her sobs with hers doorin' that weddin' ordeal. The old
ladies present shakes their heads a heap solemn.

" ' "It's a worse augoory," says one, "than the hoots
of a score of squinch owls."

" 'When this reign of terror is at its height, the local
eye is rolled appealin'ly towards us Chevy Chasers. We
rises to the opportoonity. Day after day we're ridin' the
hills an' vales, readin' the milk white snow for tracks.
An' we has success. One mornin' I comes up on two of
the Brackenridge boys an' five more of the Chevy Chasers
settin' on their hosses at the Skinner cross roads. Bob
Crittenden's gone to turn me out, they says. Then they
p'ints down to a handful of close-wove bresh an' stunted
timber an' allows that this maraudin' cat-o-mount is hid-
in' thar; they sees him go skulkin' in.

" 'Gents, I ain't above admittin' that the news puts my heart to a canter. I'm brave; but conflicts with wild an' savage beasts is to me a novelty an' while I faces my fate without a flutter, I'm yere to say I'd sooner been in pursoot of minks or raccoons or some varmint whose grievous cap'bilities I can more ackerately stack up an' in whose merry ways I'm better versed. However, the dauntless blood of my grandsire mounts in my cheek; an' as if the shade of that old Trojan is thar personal to su'gest it, I searches forth a flask an' renoos my sperit; thus qualified for perils, come in what form they may, I resolootely stands my hand.

" 'Thar's forty dogs if thar's one in our company as we pauses at the Skinner cross-roads. An' when the Crittenden yooth returns, he brings with him the Rickett boys an' forty added dogs. Which it's worth a ten-mile ride to get a glimpse of that outfit of canines! Thar's every sort onder the canopy: thar's the stolid hound, the alert fice, the sapient collie; that is thar's individyool beasts wherein the hound, or fice, or collie seems to preedominate as a strain. The trooth is thar's not that dog a-whinin' about our hosses' fetlocks who ain't proudly descended from fifteen different tribes, an' they shorely makes a motley mass meetin'. Still, they're good, zealous dogs; an' as they're going to go for'ard an' take most of the resks of that panther, it seems invidious to criticize 'em.

" 'One of the Twitty boys rides down an' puts the eighty or more dogs into the bresh. The rest of us lays back an' strains our eyes. Thar he is! A shout goes up as we descries the panther stealin' off by a far corner. He's headin' along a hollow that's full of bresh an' baby timber an' runs parallel with the pike. Big an' yaller he is; we can tell from the slight flash we gets of him as he darts into a second clump of bushes. With a cry—what

young Crittenden calls a "view halloo,"—we goes stam-
peedin' down the pike in pursoot.

" 'Our dogs is sta'nch; they shore does themse'fs proud.
Singin' in twenty keys, reachin' from growls to yelps an'
from yelps to shrillest screams, they pushes dauntlessly
on the fresh trail of their terrified quarry. Now an' then
we gets a squint of the panther as he skulks from one
copse to another jest ahead. Which he's goin' like a
arrow; no mistake! As for us Chevy Chasers, we paral-
lels the hunt, an' continyoos poundin' the Skinner turn-
pike abreast of the pack, ever an' anon givin' a encour-
agin' shout as we briefly sights our game.

" 'Gents,' says Colonel Sterett, as he ag'in refreshes
hims'ef, 'it's needless to go over that hunt in detail. We
hustles the flyin' demon full eighteen miles, our faithful
dogs crowdin' close an' breathless at his coward heels.
Still, they don't catch up with him; he streaks it like some
saffron meteor.

" 'Only once does we approach within strikin' distance;
that's when he crosses at old Stafford's whisky still. As
he glides into view, Crittenden shouts:

" ' "Thar he goes!"'

" 'For myse'f I'm prepared. I've got one of these mis-
guided cap-an'-ball six-shooters that's built doorin' the
war; an' I cuts that hardware loose! This weapon seems
a born profligate of lead, for the six chambers goes off
together. Which you should have seen the Chevy Chasers
dodge! An' well they may; that broadside ain't in vain!
My aim is so troo that one of the r'armost dogs evolves a
howl an' rolls over; then he sets up gnawin' an' lickin' his
off hind laig in frantic alternations. That hunt is done
for him. We leaves him doctorin' himse'f an' picks him
up two hours later on our triumphant return.

" 'As I states, we harries that foogitive panther for

eighteen miles an' in our hot ardor founders two hosses. Fatigue an' weariness begins to overpower us; also our prey weakens along with the rest. In the half glimpses we now an' ag'in gets of him it's plain that both pace an' distance is tellin' fast. Still, he presses on; an' as thar's no spur like fear, that panther holds his distance.

" 'But the end comes. We've done run him into a rough, wild stretch of country where settlements is few an' cabins roode. Of a sudden, the panther emerges onto the road an' goes rackin' along the trail. We pushes our spent steeds to the utmost.

" 'Thar's a log house ahead; out in the stump-filled lot in front is a frowsy woman an' five small children. The panther leaps the rickety worm-fence an' heads straight as a bullet for the cl'arin! Horrors! the sight freezes our marrows! Mad an' savage, he's doo to bite a hunk outen that devoted household! Mutooally callin' to each other, we goads our horses to the utmost. We gain on the panther! He may wound but he won't have time to slay that fam'ly.

" 'Gents, it's a soopreme moment! The panther makes for the female squatter an' her litter, we pantin' an' pressin' clost behind. The panther is among 'em; the woman an' the children seems transfixed by the awful spectacle an' stands rooted with open eyes an' mouths. Our emotions shore beggars deescriptions.

" 'Now ensooes a scene to smite the hardiest of us with dismay. No sooner does the panther find himse'f in the midst of that he'pless bevy of little ones, than he stops, turns round abrupt, an' sets down on his tail; an' then upliftin' his muzzle he busts into shrieks an' yells an' howls an' cries, a complete case of dog hysterics! That's what he is, a great yeller dog; his reason is now a wrack because we harasses him the eighteen miles.

" 'Thar's a ugly outcast of a squatter, mattock in hand, comes tumblin' down the hillside from some'ers out back of the shanty where he's been grubbin':

" ' "What be you-all eediots chasin' my dog for?" demands this onkempt party. Then he menaces us with the implement.

" 'We makes no retort but stands passive. The great orange brute whose nerves has been torn to rags creeps to the squatter an' with mournful howls explains what we've made him suffer.

" 'No, thar's nothin' further to do an' less to be said. That cavalcade, erstwhile so gala an' buoyant, drags itself wearily homeward, the exhausted dogs in the r'ar walkin' stiff an' sore like their laigs is wood. For more'n a mile the complainin' howls of the hysterical yeller dog is wafted to our years. Then they ceases; an' we figgers his sympathizin' master has done took him into the shanty an' shet the door.

" 'No one comments on this adventure, not a word is heard. Each is silent ontil we mounts the Big Murray hill. As we collects ourse'fs on this eminence one of the Brackenridge boys holds up his hand for a halt. "Gents," he says, as—hosses, hunters an' dogs—we-all gathers 'round, "gents, I moves you the Chevy Chase Huntin' Club yereby stands adjourned *sine die*." Thar's a moment's pause, an' then as by one impulse every gent, hoss an' dog, says "Ay!" It's yoonanimous, an' from that hour till now the Chevy Chase Huntin' Club ain't been nothin' save tradition. But that panther shore disappears; it's the end of his vandalage; an' ag'in does quadrilles, pra'rs, an poker resoom their wonted sway. That's the end; an' now, gents, if Black Jack will caper to his dooties we'll uplift our drooped energies with the usual forty drops.' "

# WOUTER VAN TWILLER

BY WASHINGTON IRVING

It was in the year of our Lord 1629 that Mynheer Wouter Van Twiller was appointed governor of the province of Nieuw Nederlandts, under the commission and control of their High Mightinesses the Lords States General of the United Netherlands, and the privileged West India Company.

This renowned old gentleman arrived at New Amsterdam in the merry month of June, the sweetest month in all the year; when dan Apollo seems to dance up the transparent firmament,—when the robin, the thrush, and a thousand other wanton songsters make the woods to resound with amorous ditties, and the luxurious little boblincoln revels among the clover-blossoms of the meadows, —all which happy coincidence persuaded the old dames of New Amsterdam, who were skilled in the art of foretelling events, that this was to be a happy and prosperous administration.

The renowned Wouter (or Walter) Van Twiller was descended from a long line of Dutch burgomasters, who had successively dozed away their lives and grown fat upon the bench of magistracy in Rotterdam; and who had comported themselves with such singular wisdom and propriety, that they were never either heard or talked of —which, next to being universally applauded, should be the object of ambition of all magistrates and rulers.

There are two opposite ways by which some men make a figure in the world; one, by talking faster than they think, and the other, by holding their tongues and not thinking at all. By the first, many a smatterer acquires the reputation of a man of quick parts; by the other, many a dunderpate, like the owl, the stupidest of birds, comes to be considered the very type of wisdom. This, by the way, is a casual remark, which I would not, for the universe, have it thought I apply to Governor Van Twiller. It is true he was a man shut up within himself, like an oyster, and rarely spoke, except in monosyllables; but then it was allowed he seldom said a foolish thing. So invincible was his gravity that he was never known to laugh or even to smile through the whole course of a long and prosperous life. Nay, if a joke were uttered in his presence, that set light-minded hearers in a roar, it was observed to throw him into a state of perplexity. Sometimes he would deign to inquire into the matter, and when, after much explanation, the joke was made as plain as a pike-staff, he would continue to smoke his pipe in silence, and at length, knocking out the ashes, would exclaim, "Well, I see nothing in all that to laugh about."

With all his reflective habits, he never made up his mind on a subject. His adherents accounted for this by the astonishing magnitude of his ideas. He conceived every subject on so grand a scale that he had not room in his head to turn it over and examine both sides of it. Certain it is, that if any matter were propounded to him on which ordinary mortals would rashly determine at first glance, he would put on a vague, mysterious look, shake his capacious head, smoke some time in profound silence, and at length observe, that "he had his doubts about the matter"; which gained him the reputation of a man slow of belief and not easily imposed upon. What is more, it gained him a lasting name; for to this habit of the mind has been attributed his surname of Twiller; which is said to be a corruption of the original Twijfler, or, in plain English, *Doubter.*

The person of this illustrious old gentleman was formed and proportioned as though it had been moulded by the hands of some cunning Dutch statuary, as a model of majesty and lordly grandeur. He was exactly five feet six inches in height, and six feet five inches in circumference. His head was a perfect sphere, and of such stupendous dimensions, that Dame Nature, with all her sex's ingenuity, would have been puzzled to construct a neck capable of supporting it; wherefore she wisely declined the attempt, and settled it firmly on the top of his backbone, just between the shoulders. His body was oblong, and particularly capacious at bottom; which was wisely ordered by Providence, seeing that he was a man of sedentary habits, and very averse to the idle labor of walking. His legs were short, but sturdy in proportion to the weight they had to sustain; so that when erect he had not a little the appearance of a beer barrel on skids. His face, that infallible index of the mind, presented a vast expanse, unfurrowed by those lines and angles which disfigure the human countenance with what is termed expression. Two small gray eyes twinkled feebly in the midst, like two stars of lesser magnitude in a hazy firmament, and his full-fed cheeks, which seemed to have taken toll of everything that went into his mouth, were curiously mottled and streaked with dusty red, like a spitzenberg apple.

His habits were as regular as his person. He daily took his four stated meals, appropriating exactly an hour to each; he smoked and doubted eight hours, and he slept the remaining twelve of the four-and-twenty. Such was

the renowned Wouter Van Twiller,—a true philosopher,
for his mind was either elevated above, or tranquilly settled below, the cares and perplexities of this world. He
had lived in it for years, without feeling the least curiosity to know whether the sun revolved round it, or it round
the sun; and he had watched, for at least half a century,
the smoke curling from his pipe to the ceiling, without
once troubling his head with any of those numerous
theories by which a philosopher would have perplexed his
brain, in accounting for its rising above the surrounding
atmosphere.

In his council he presided with great state and solemnity. He sat in a huge chair of solid oak, hewn in the
celebrated forest of the Hague, fabricated by an experienced timmerman of Amsterdam, and curiously carved
about the arms and feet into exact imitations of gigantic
eagle's claws. Instead of a scepter, he swayed a long
Turkish pipe, wrought with jasmin and amber, which
had been presented to a stadtholder of Holland at the
conclusion of a treaty with one of the petty Barbary powers. In this stately chair would he sit, and this magnificent pipe would he smoke, shaking his right knee with a
constant motion, and fixing his eye for hours together
upon a little print of Amsterdam, which hung in a black
frame against the opposite wall of the council-chamber.
Nay, it has even been said, that when any deliberation of
extraordinary length and intricacy was on the carpet, the
renowned Wouter would shut his eyes for full two hours
at a time, that he might not be disturbed by external ob-
jects; and at such times the internal commotion of his
mind was evinced by certain regular guttural sounds,
which his admirers declared were merely the noise of con-
flict, made by his contending doubts and opinions.

It is with infinite difficulty I have been enabled to collect these biographical anecdotes of the great man under consideration. The facts respecting him were so scattered and vague, and divers of them so questionable in point of authenticity, that I have had to give up the search after many, and decline the admission of still more, which would have tended to heighten the coloring of his portrait.

I have been the more anxious to delineate fully the person and habits of Wouter Van Twiller, from the consideration that he was not only the first, but also the best governor that ever presided over this ancient and respectable province; and so tranquil and benevolent was his reign, that I do not find throughout the whole of it a single instance of any offender being brought to punishment,—a most indubitable sign of a merciful governor, and a case unparalleled, excepting in the reign of the illustrious King Log, from whom, it is hinted, the renowned Van Twiller was a lineal descendant.

The very outset of the career of this excellent magistrate was distinguished by an example of legal acumen, that gave flattering presage of a wise and equitable administration. The morning after he had been installed in office, and at the moment that he was making his breakfast from a prodigious earthen dish, filled with milk and Indian pudding, he was interrupted by the appearance of Wandle Schoonhoven, a very important old burgher of New Amsterdam, who complained bitterly of one Barent Bleecker, inasmuch as he refused to come to a settlement of accounts, seeing that there was a heavy balance in favor of the said Wandle. Governor Van Twiller, as I have already observed, was a man of few words; he was likewise a mortal enemy to multiplying writings—or being disturbed at his breakfast. Having listened attentively to the statement of Wandle Schoonhoven, giving an occasional grunt, as he shoveled a spoonful of Indian pudding into his mouth,—either as a sign that he relished the dish, or comprehended the story,—he called unto him his constable, and pulling out of his breeches-pocket a huge jack-knife, dispatched it after the defendant as a summons, accompanied by his tobacco-box as a warrant.

This summary process was as effectual in those simple days as was the seal-ring of the great Haroun Alraschid among the true believers. The two parties being confronted before him, each produced a book of accounts, written in a language and character that would have puzzled any but a High-Dutch commentator, or a learned decipherer of Egyptian obelisks. The sage Wouter took them one after the other, and having poised them in his hands, and attentively counted over the number of leaves, fell straightway into a very great doubt, and smoked for half an hour without saying a word; at length, laying his finger beside his nose, and shutting his eyes for a moment, with the air of a man who has just caught a subtle idea by the tail, he slowly took his pipe from his mouth, puffed forth a column of tobacco-smoke, and with marvelous gravity and solemnity pronounced, that, having carefully counted over the leaves and weighed the books, it was found, that one was just as thick and as heavy as the other: therefore, it was the final opinion of the court that the accounts were equally balanced: therefore, Wandle should give Barent a receipt, and Barent should give Wandle a receipt, and the constable should pay the costs.

This decision, being straightway made known, diffused general joy throughout New Amsterdam, for the people immediately perceived that they had a very wise and equitable magistrate to rule over them. But its happiest effect was, that not another lawsuit took place throughout the whole of his administration; and the office of constable fell into such decay, that there was not one of those losel scouts known in the province for many years. I am the more particular in dwelling on this transaction, not only because I deem it one of the most sage and righteous judgments on record, and well worthy the attention of modern magistrates, but because it was a miraculous event in the history of the renowned Wouter—being the only time he was ever known to come to a decision in the whole course of his life.

# THE EXPERIENCES OF THE A. C.

BY BAYARD TAYLOR

"Bridgeport! Change cars for the Naugatuck Railroad!" shouted the conductor of the New York and Boston Express Train, on the evening of May 27, 1858. . . . Mr. Johnson, carpet-bag in hand, jumped upon the platform, entered the office, purchased a ticket for Waterbury, and was soon whirling in the Naugatuck train towards his destination.

On reaching Waterbury, in the soft spring twilight, Mr. Johnson walked up and down in front of the station, curiously scanning the faces of the assembled crowd. Presently he noticed a gentleman who was performing the same operation upon the faces of the alighting passengers. Throwing himself directly in the way of the latter, the two exchanged a steady gaze.

"Is your name Billings?" "Is your name Johnson?" were simultaneous questions, followed by the simultaneous exclamations,—"Ned!" "Enos!"

Then there was a crushing grasp of hands, repeated after a pause, in testimony of ancient friendship, and Mr. Billings, returning to practical life, asked:

"Is that all your baggage? Come, I have a buggy here: Eunice has heard the whistle, and she 'll be impatient to welcome you."

The impatience of Eunice (Mrs. Billings, of course) was not of long duration; for in five minutes thereafter she stood at the door of her husband's chocolate-colored villa, receiving his friend. . . .

J. Edward Johnson was a tall, thin gentleman of forty-five. . . . A year before, some letters, signed "Foster, Kirkup & Co., per Enos Billings," had accidently revealed to him the whereabouts of the old friend of his youth, with whom we now find him domiciled. . . .

"Enos," said he, as he stretched out his hand for the third cup of tea (which he had taken only for the purpose of prolonging the pleasant table-chat), "I wonder which of us is most changed."

"You, of course," said Mr. Billings, "with your brown face and big moustache. Your own brother would n't have known you, if he had seen you last, as I did, with smooth cheeks and hair of unmerciful length. Why, not even your voice is the same!"

"That is easily accounted for," replied Mr. Johnson. "But in your case, Enos, I am puzzled to find where the difference lies. Your features seem to be but little changed, now that I can examine them at leisure; yet it is not the same face. But really, I never looked at you for so long a time, in those days. I beg pardon; you used to be so—so remarkably shy."

Mr. Billings blushed slightly, and seemed at a loss what to answer. His wife, however, burst into a merry laugh, exclaiming:

"Oh, that was before the days of the A. C.!"

He, catching the infection, laughed also; in fact, Mr. Johnson laughed, but without knowing why.

"The 'A. C.'!" said Mr. Billings. "Bless me, Eunice! how long it is since we have talked of that summer! I had almost forgotten that there ever was an A. C. . . . Well, the A. C. culminated in '45. You remember something of the society of Norridgeport, the last winter you were there? Abel Mallory, for instance?"

"Let me think a moment," said Mr. Johnson, reflectively. "Really, it seems like looking back a hundred years. Mallory,—was n't that the sentimental young man, with wispy hair, a tallowy skin, and big, sweaty hands, who used to be spouting Carlyle on the 'reading evenings' at Shelldrake's? Yes, to be sure; and there was Hollins, with his clerical face and infidel talk,— and Pauline Ringtop, who used to say, 'The Beautiful is the Good.' I can still hear her shrill voice singing, 'Would that *I* were beautiful, would that *I* were fair!' "

There was a hearty chorus of laughter at poor Miss Ringtop's expense. It harmed no one, however; for the tar-weed was already becoming thick over her Californian grave.

"Oh, I see," said Mr. Billings, "you still remember the absurdities of those days. In fact, I think you partially saw through them then. But I was younger, and far from being so clear-headed, and I looked upon those evenings at Shelldrake's as being equal, at least, to the *symposia* of Plato. Something in Mallory always repelled me. I detested the sight of his thick nose, with the flaring nostrils, and his coarse, half-formed lips, of the bluish color of raw corned-beef. But I looked upon these feelings as unreasonable prejudices, and strove to conquer them, seeing the admiration which he received from others. He was an oracle on the subject of 'Nature.' Having eaten nothing for two years, except Graham bread, vegetables without salt, and fruits, fresh or dried, he considered himself to have attained an antediluvian purity of health,—or that he would attain it, so soon as two pimples on his left temple should have healed. These pimples he looked upon as the last feeble stand made by the pernicious juices left from the meat he had formerly eaten and the coffee he had drunk. His theory was, that through a body so purged and purified none but true and natural impulses could find access to the soul. Such, indeed, was the theory we all held. . . .

"Shelldrake was a man of more pretense than real cultivation, as I afterwards discovered. He was in good circumstances, and always glad to receive us at his house, as this made him virtually the chief of our tribe, and the outlay for refreshments involved only the apples from his own orchard, and water from his well. . . .

"Well, 't was in the early part of '45,—I think in April,—when we were all gathered together, discussing, as usual, the possibility of leading a life in accordance with Nature. Abel Mallory was there, and Hollins, and Miss Ringtop, and Faith Levis, with her knitting,—and also Eunice Hazleton, a lady whom you have never seen, but you may take my wife as her representative. . . .

"I wish I could recollect some of the speeches made on that occasion. Abel had but one pimple on his temple (there was a purple spot where the other had been), and was estimating that in two or three months more he would be a true, unspoiled man. His complexion, nevertheless, was more clammy and whey-like than ever.

" 'Yes,' said he, 'I also am an Arcadian! This false dual existence which I have been leading will soon be merged in the unity of Nature. Our lives must conform to her sacred law. Why can't we strip off these hollow Shams' (he made great use of that word), 'and be our true selves, pure, perfect, and divine?' . . .

"Shelldrake, however, turning to his wife, said,—

" 'Elviry, how many up-stairs rooms is there in that house down on the Sound?'

" 'Four,—besides three small ones under the roof. Why, what made you think of that, Jesse?' said she.

" 'I've got an idea, while Abel's been talking,' he answered. 'We 've taken a house for the summer, down the other side of Bridgeport, right on the water, where there's good fishing and a fine view of the Sound. Now, there's room enough for all of us,—at least, all that can make it suit to go. Abel, you and Enos, and Pauline and Eunice might fix matters so that we could all take the place in partnership, and pass the summer together, living a true and beautiful life in the bosom of Nature. There we shall be perfectly free and untrammelled by the chains which still hang around us in Norridgeport. You know how often we have wanted to be set on some island in the Pacific Ocean, where we could build up a true society, right from the start. Now, here's a chance to try the experiment for a few months, anyhow.'

"Eunice clapped her hands (yes, you did!) and cried out,—

"'Splendid! Arcadian! I'll give up my school for the summer.' . . .

"Abel Mallory, of course, did not need to have the proposal repeated. He was ready for anything which promised indolence and the indulgence of his sentimental tastes. I will do the fellow the justice to say that he was not a hypocrite. He firmly believed both in himself and his ideas,—especially the former. He pushed both hands through the long wisps of his drab-colored hair, and threw his head back until his wide nostrils resembled a double door to his brain.

"'O Nature!' he said, 'you have found your lost children! We shall obey your neglected laws! we shall hearken to your divine whispers! we shall bring you back from your ignominious exile, and place you on your ancestral throne!' . . .

"The company was finally arranged to consist of the Shelldrakes, Hollins, Mallory, Eunice, Miss Ringtop, and myself. We did not give much thought, either to the preparations in advance, or to our mode of life when settled there. We were to live near to Nature: that was the main thing.

" 'What shall we call the place?' asked Eunice.

" 'Arcadia!' said Abel Mallory, rolling up his large green eyes.

" 'Then,' said Hollins, 'let us constitute ourselves the Arcadian Club!' "

—"Aha!" interrupted Mr. Johnson, "I see! The A. C.!"

"Yes, you see the A. C. now, but to understand it fully you should have had a share in those Arcadian experiences. . . . It was a lovely afternoon in June when we first approached Arcadia. . . . Perkins Brown, Shelldrake's boy-of-all-work, awaited us at the door. He had been sent on two or three days in advance, to take charge of the house, and seemed to have had enough of hermit-life, for he hailed us with a wild whoop, throwing his straw hat half-way up one of the poplars. Perkins was a boy of fifteen, the child of poor parents, who were satisfied to get him off their hands, regardless as to what humanitarian theories might be tested upon him. As the Arcadian Club recognized no such thing as caste, he was always admitted to our meetings, and understood just enough of our conversation to excite a silly ambition in his slow mind. . . .

"Our board, that evening, was really tempting. The absence of meat was compensated to us by the crisp and racy onions, and I craved only a little salt, which had been interdicted, as a most pernicious substance. I sat at one corner of the table, beside Perkins Brown, who took an opportunity, while the others were engaged in conversation, to jog my elbow gently. As I turned towards him, he said nothing, but dropped his eyes significantly. The little rascal had the lid of a blacking-box, filled with salt, upon his knee, and was privately seasoning his onions and radishes. I blushed at the thought of my hypocrisy, but the onions were so much better that I could n't help dipping into the lid with him.

" 'Oh,' said Eunice, 'we must send for some oil and vinegar! This lettuce is very nice.'

" 'Oil and vinegar?' exclaimed Abel.

" 'Why, yes,' said she, innocently: 'they are both vegetable substances.'

"Abel at first looked rather foolish, but quickly recovering himself, said,—

" 'All vegetable substances are not proper for food: you would not taste the poison-oak, or sit under the upas-tree of Java.'

" 'Well, Abel,' Eunice rejoined, 'how are we to distinguish what is best for us? How are we to know *what* vegetables to choose, or what animal and mineral substances to avoid?'

" 'I will tell you,' he answered, with a lofty air. 'See here!' pointing to his temple, where the second pimple—either from the change of air, or because, in the excitement of the last few days, he had forgotten it—was actually healed. 'My blood is at last pure. The struggle between the natural and the unnatural is over, and I am beyond the depraved influences of my former taste. My instincts are now, therefore, entirely pure also. What is good for man to eat, that I shall have a natural desire to eat: what is bad will be naturally repelled. How does the cow distinguish between the wholesome and the poisonous herbs of the meadow? And is man less than a cow, that he can not cultivate his instincts to an equal point? Let me walk through the woods and I can tell you every berry and root which God designed for food, though I know not its name, and have never seen it before. I shall make use of my time, during our sojourn here, to test, by my purified instinct, every substance, animal, mineral, and vegetable, upon which the human race subsists, and to create a catalogue of the True Food of Man!' . . .

"Our lazy life during the hot weather had become a little monotonous. The Arcadian plan had worked tolerably well, on the whole, for there was very little for any one to do,—Mrs. Shelldrake and Perkins Brown excepted. Our conversation, however, lacked spirit and variety. We were, perhaps unconsciously, a little tired of hearing and assenting to the same sentiments. But, one evening, about this time, Hollins struck upon a variation, the consequences of which he little foresaw. We had been reading one of Bulwer's works (the weather was too hot for Psychology), and came upon this paragraph, or something like it:

" 'Ah, Behind the Veil! We see the summer smile of the Earth,—enamelled meadow and limpid stream,—but what hides she in her sunless heart? Caverns of serpents, or grottoes of priceless gems? Youth, whose soul sits on thy countenance, thyself wearing no mask, strive not to lift the masks of others! Be content with what thou seest; and wait until Time and Experience shall teach thee to find jealousy behind the sweet smile, and hatred under the honeyed word!'

"This seemed to us a dark and bitter reflection; but one or another of us recalled some illustration of human hypocrisy, and the evidences, by the simple fact of repetition, gradually led to a division of opinion,—Hollins, Shelldrake, and Miss Ringtop on the dark side, and the rest of us on the bright. The last, however, contented herself with quoting from her favorite poet Gamaliel J. Gawthrop:

" 'I look beyond thy brow's concealment!
I see thy spirit's dark revealment!
Thy inner self betrayed I see:
Thy coward, craven, shivering ME.'

" 'We think we know one another,' exclaimed Hollins;
'but do we? We see the faults of others, their weaknesses, their disagreeable qualities, and we keep silent.
How much we should gain, were candor as universal as
concealment! Then each one, seeing himself as others see
him, would truly know himself. How much misunder-
standing might be avoided, how much hidden shame be
removed, hopeless because unspoken love made glad,
honest admiration cheer its object, uttered sympathy
mitigate misfortune,—in short, how much brighter and
happier the world would become, if each one expressed,
everywhere and at all times, his true and entire feeling!
Why, even Evil would lose half its power!'

"There seemed to be so much practical wisdom in these
views that we were all dazzled and half-convinced at the
start. So, when Hollins, turning towards me, as he continued, exclaimed,—'Come, why should not this candor
be adopted in our Arcadia? Will any one—will you,
Enos—commence at once by telling me now—to my face
—my principal faults?' I answered, after a moment's
reflection,—'You have a great deal of intellectual arro-
gance, and you are, physically, very indolent.'

"He did not flinch from the self-invited test, though he
looked a little surprised.

" 'Well put,' said he, 'though I do not say that you are
entirely correct. Now, what are my merits?'

" 'You are clear-sighted,' I answered, 'an earnest seeker
after truth, and courageous in the avowal of your
thoughts.'

"This restored the balance, and we soon began to confess our own private faults and weaknesses. Though the confessions did not go very deep,—no one betraying any thing we did not all know already,—yet they were sufficient to strengthen Hollins in his new idea, and it was unanimously resolved that Candor should thenceforth be the main charm of our Arcadian life. . . .

"The next day, Abel, who had resumed his researches after the True Food, came home to supper with a healthier color than I had before seen on his face.

" 'Do you know,' said he, looking shyly at Hollins, 'that I begin to think Beer must be a natural beverage? There was an auction in the village to-day, as I passed through, and I stopped at a cake-stand to get a glass of water, as it was very hot. There was no water,—only beer: so I thought I would try a glass, simply as an experiment. Really, the flavor was very agreeable. And it occurred to me, on the way home, that all the elements contained in beer are vegetable. Besides, fermentation is a natural process. I think the question has never been properly tested before.'

" 'But the alcohol!' exclaimed Hollins.

" 'I could not distinguish any, either by taste or smell. I know that chemical analysis is said to show it; but may not the alcohol be created, somehow, during the analysis?'

" 'Abel,' said Hollins, in a fresh burst of candor, 'you will never be a Reformer, until you possess some of the commonest elements of knowledge.'

"The rest of us were much diverted: it was a pleasant relief to our monotonous amiability.

"Abel, however, had a stubborn streak in his character. The next day he sent Perkins Brown to Bridgeport for a dozen bottles of 'Beer.' Perkins, either intentionally or by mistake, (I always suspected the former,) brought pint-bottles of Scotch ale, which he placed in the coolest part of the cellar. The evening happened to be exceedingly hot and sultry; and, as we were all fanning ourselves and talking languidly, Abel bethought him of his beer. In his thirst, he drank the contents of the first bottle, almost at a single draught.

" 'The effect of beer,' said he, 'depends, I think, on the commixture of the nourishing principle of the grain with the cooling properties of the water. Perhaps, hereafter, a liquid food of the same character may be invented, which shall save us from mastication and all the diseases of the teeth.'

"Hollins and Shelldrake, at his invitation, divided a bottle between them, and he took a second. The potent beverage was not long in acting on a brain so unaccustomed to its influence. He grew unusually talkative and sentimental, in a few minutes.

" 'Oh, sing, somebody!' he sighed in hoarse rapture: 'the night was made for Song.'

"Miss Ringtop, nothing loath, immediately commenced, 'When stars are in the quiet skies'; but scarcely had she finished the first verse before Abel interrupted her.

" 'Candor's the order of the day, isn't it?' he asked.

" 'Yes!' 'Yes!' two or three answered.

" 'Well, then,' said he, 'candidly, Pauline, you've got the darn'dest squeaky voice'—

"Miss Ringtop gave a faint little scream of horror.

" 'Oh, never mind!' he continued. 'We act according to impulse, don't we? And I've the impulse to swear; and it's right. Let Nature have her way. Listen! Damn, damn, damn, damn! I never knew it was so easy. Why, there's a pleasure in it! Try it, Pauline! try it on me!'

" 'Oh-ooh!' was all Miss Ringtop could utter.

" 'Abel! Abel!' exclaimed Hollins, 'the beer has got into your head.'

" 'No, it isn't Beer,—it's Candor!' said Abel. "It's your own proposal, Hollins. Suppose it's evil to swear: isn't it better I should express it, and be done with it, than keep it bottled up, to ferment in my mind? Oh, you're a precious, consistent old humbug, *you* are!'

"And therewith he jumped off the stoop, and went dancing awkwardly down toward the water, singing in a most unmelodious voice, ' 'T is home where'er the heart is.' . . .

"We had an unusually silent breakfast the next morning. Abel scarcely spoke, which the others attributed to a natural feeling of shame, after his display of the previous evening. Hollins and Shelldrake discussed Temperance, with a special view to his edification, and Miss Ringtop favored us with several quotations about 'the maddening bowl,'—but he paid no attention to them. . . .

"The forenoon was overcast, with frequent showers. Each one occupied his or her room until dinner-time, when we met again with something of the old geniality. There was an evident effort to restore our former flow of good feeling. Abel's experience with the beer was freely discussed. He insisted strongly that he had not been laboring under its effects, and proposed a mutual test. He, Shelldrake, and Hollins were to drink it in equal measures, and compare observations as to their physical sensations. The others agreed,—quite willingly, I thought,—but I refused. . . .

"There was a sound of loud voices, as we approached the stoop. Hollins, Shelldrake and his wife, and Abel Mallory were sitting together near the door. Perkins Brown, as usual, was crouched on the lowest step, with one leg over the other, and rubbing the top of his boot with a vigor which betrayed to me some secret mirth. He looked up at me from under his straw hat with the grin of a malicious Puck, glanced toward the group, and made a curious gesture with his thumb. There were several empty pint bottles on the stoop.

" 'Now, are you sure you can bear the test?' we heard Hollins ask, as we approached.

" 'Bear it? Why, to be sure!' replied Shelldrake; 'if I couldn't bear it, or if *you* couldn't, your theory's done for. Try! I can stand it as long as you can.'

" 'Well, then,' said Hollins, 'I think you are a very ordinary man. I derive no intellectual benefit from my intercourse with you, but your house is convenient to me. I'm under no obligations for your hospitality, however, because my company is an advantage to you. Indeed, if I were treated according to my deserts, you couldn't do enough for me.'

"Mrs. Shelldrake was up in arms.

" 'Indeed,' she exclaimed, 'I think you get as good as you deserve, and more, too.'

" 'Elvira,' said he, with a benevolent condescension, 'I have no doubt you think so, for your mind belongs to the lowest and most material sphere. You have your place in Nature, and you fill it; but it is not for you to judge of intelligences which move only on the upper planes.'

" 'Hollins,' said Shelldrake, 'Elviry's a good wife and a sensible woman, and I won't allow you to turn up your nose at her.'

" 'I am not surprised,' he answered, 'that you should fail to stand the test. I didn't expect it.'

" 'Let me try it on *you!*' cried Shelldrake. 'You, now, have some intellect,—I don't deny that,—but not so much, by a long shot, as you think you have. Besides that, you're awfully selfish in your opinions. You won't admit that anybody can be right who differs from you. You've sponged on me for a long time; but I suppose I've learned something from you, so we'll call it even. I think, however, that what you call acting according to impulse is simply an excuse to cover your own laziness.'

" 'Gosh! that's it!' interrupted Perkins, jumping up; then, recollecting himself, he sank down on the steps again, and shook with a suppressed 'Ho! ho! ho!'

"Hollins, however, drew himself up with an exasperated air.

" 'Shelldrake,' said he, 'I pity you. I always knew your ignorance, but I thought you honest in your human character. I never suspected you of envy and malice. However, the true Reformer must expect to be misunderstood and misrepresented by meaner minds. That love which I bear to all creatures teaches me to forgive you. Without such love, all plans of progress must fail. Is it not so, Abel?' "

"Shelldrake could only ejaculate the words, 'Pity!' 'Forgive!' in his most contemptuous tone; while Mrs. Shelldrake, rocking violently in her chair, gave utterance to the peculiar clucking *'ts, ts, ts, ts,'* whereby certain women express emotions too deep for words.

"Abel, roused by Hollins' question, answered, with a sudden energy:

" 'Love! there is no love in the world. Where will you find it? Tell me, and I'll go there. Love! I'd like to see it! If all human hearts were like mine, we might have an Arcadia; but most men have no hearts. The world is a miserable, hollow, deceitful shell of vanity and hypocrisy. No: let us give up. We were born before our time: this age is not worthy of us.'

"Hollins stared at the speaker in utter amazement. Shelldrake gave a long whistle, and finally gasped out:

" 'Well, what next?'

"None of us were prepared for such a sudden and complete wreck of our Arcadian scheme. The foundations had been sapped before, it is true; but we had not perceived it; and now, in two short days, the whole edifice tumbled about our ears. Though it was inevitable, we felt a shock of sorrow, and a silence fell upon us. Only that scamp of a Perkins Brown, chuckling and rubbing his boot, really rejoiced. I could have kicked him.

"We all went to bed, feeling that the charm of our Arcadian life was over. . . . In the first revulsion of feeling, I was perhaps unjust to my associates. I see now, more clearly, the causes of those vagaries, which originated in a genuine aspiration, and failed from an ignorance of the true nature of Man, quite as much as from the egotism of the individuals. Other attempts at reorganizing Society were made about the same time by men of culture and experience, but in the A. C. we had neither. Our leaders had caught a few half-truths, which, in their minds, were speedily warped into errors." . . .

# WHAT MR. ROBINSON THINKS

## BY JAMES RUSSELL LOWELL

Guvener B. is a sensible man;
  He stays to his home an' looks arter his folks;
He draws his furrer ez straight ez he can,
  An' into nobody's tater-patch pokes;
         But John P.
         Robinson he
Sez he wunt vote fer Guvener B.


My! ain't it terrible? Wut shall we du?
  We can't never choose him, o' course,—thet's flat;
Guess we shall hev to come round (don't you?)
  An' go in fer thunder an' guns, an' all that;
         Fer John P.
         Robinson he
Sez he wunt vote fer Guvener B.


Gineral C. is a dreffle smart man:
  He's ben on all sides thet give places or pelf;
But consistency still was a part of his plan,—
  He's ben true to *one* party,—an' thet is himself;—
         So John P.
         Robinson he
Sez he shall vote fer Gineral C.

Gineral C. he goes in fer the war;
   He don't vally principle more'n an old cud;
Wut did God make us raytional creeturs fer,
   But glory an' gunpowder, plunder an' blood?
            So John P.
            Robinson he
Sez he shall vote for Gineral C.


We were gettin' on nicely up here to our village,
   With good old idees o' wut's right an' wut ain't,
We kind o' thought Christ went agin war an' pillage,
   An' thet eppyletts worn't the best mark of a saint;
            But John P.
            Robinson he
Sez this kind o' thing's an exploded idee.


The side of our country must ollers be took,
   An' Presidunt Polk, you know, *he* is our country,
An' the angel thet writes all our sins in a book
   Puts the *debit* to him, an' to us the *per contry;*
            An' John P.
            Robinson he
Sez this is his view o' the thing to a T.


Parson Wilbur he calls all these argimunts lies;
   Sez they're nothin' on airth but jest *fee, faw, fum;*
An' thet all this big talk of our destinies
   Is half on it ign'ance, an' t' other half rum;
            But John P.
            Robinson he
Sez it ain't no sech thing; an', of course, so must we.

Parson Wilbur sez *he* never heerd in his life
   Thet th' Apostles rigged out in their swaller-tail coats,
An' marched round in front of a drum an' a fife,
   To git some on 'em office, an' some on 'em votes;
               But John P.
               Robinson he
Sez they didn't know everythin' down in Judee.


Wall, it's a marcy we've gut folks to tell us
   The rights an' the wrongs o' these matters, I vow,—
God sends country lawyers, an' other wise fellers,
   To start the world's team wen it gits in a slough;
               Fer John P.
               Robinson he
Sez the world'll go right, ef he hollers out Gee!

# THE DAY WE DO NOT CELEBRATE

BY ROBERT J. BURDETTE

One famous day in great July
John Adams said, long years gone by,

"This day that makes a people free
Shall be the people's jubilee,

"With games, guns, sports, and shows displayed,
With bells, pomp, bonfires, and parade,

"Throughout this land, from shore to shore,
From this time forth, forevermore."

The years passed on, and by and by,
Men's hearts grew cold in hot July.

And Mayor Hawarden Cholmondely said
"Hof rockets Hi ham sore hafraid;

"Hand hif you send one hup hablaze,
Hi'll send you hup for sixty days."

Then said the Mayor O'Shay McQuade,
"Thayre uz no nade fur no perade."

And Mayor Hans Von Schwartzenmeyer
Proclaimed, "I'll haf me no bonfier!"

Said Mayor Baptiste Raphael
"No make-a ring-a dat-a bell!"

## ROBERT J. BURDETTE

"By gar!" cried Mayor Jean Crapaud,
"Zis July games vill has to go!"

And Mayor Knud Christofferrssonn
Said, "Djeath to hjjim who fjjres a gjjunn!"

At last, cried Mayor Wun Lung Lee—
"Too muchee hoop-la boberee!"

And so the Yankee holiday,
Of proclamations passed away.

# THE YANKEE DUDE'LL DO

BY S. E. KISER

When Cholly swung his golf-stick on the links,
  Or knocked the tennis-ball across the net,
With his bangs done up in cunning little kinks—
  When he wore the tallest collar he could get,
    Oh, it was the fashion then
    To impale him on the pen—
To regard him as a being made of putty through and
    through;
    But his racquet's laid away,
    He is roughing it to-day,
And heroically proving that the Yankee dude'll do.


When Algy, as some knight of old arrayed,
  Was the leading figure at the "fawncy ball,"
We loathed him for the silly part he played,
  He was set down as a monkey—that was all!
    Oh, we looked upon him then
    As unfit to class with men,
As one whose heart was putty, and whose brains were
    made of glue;
    But he 's thrown his cane away,
    And he grasps a gun to-day,
While the world beholds him, knowing that the Yankee
    dude'll do.

When Clarence cruised about upon his yacht,
  Or drove out with his footman through the park,
His mamma, it was generally thought,
  Ought to have him in her keeping after dark!
    Oh, we ridiculed him then,
    We impaled him on the pen,
We thought he was effeminate, we dubbed him "Sissy,"
      too;
    But he nobly marched away,
    He is eating pork to-day,
And heroically proving that the Yankee dude'll do.


How they hurled themselves against the angry foe,
  In the jungle and the trenches on the hill!
When the word to charge was given, every dude was
    on the go—
  He was there to die, to capture, or to kill!
    Oh, he struck his level when
    Men were called upon again
To preserve the ancient glory of the old red, white, and
    blue!
    He has thrown his spats away,
    He is wearing spurs to-day,
And the world will please take notice that the Yankee
    dude'll do!

# SPELLING DOWN THE MASTER

## BY EDWARD EGGLESTON

"I 'low," said Mrs. Means, as she stuffed the tobacco into her cob pipe after supper on that eventful Wednesday evening: "I 'low they'll app'int the Squire to gin out the words to-night. They mos' always do, you see, kase he's the peartest *ole* man in this deestrick; and I 'low some of the young fellers would have to git up and dust ef they would keep up to him. And he uses sech remarkable smart words. He speaks so polite, too. But laws! don't I remember when he was poarer nor Job's turkey? Twenty year ago, when he come to these 'ere diggin's, that air Squire Hawkins was a poar Yankee school-master, that said 'pail' instid of bucket, and that called a cow a 'caow,' and that couldn't tell to save his gizzard what we meant by *'low* and by *right smart*. But he's larnt our ways now, an' he's jest as civilized as the rest of us. You would-n know he'd ever been a Yankee. He didn't stay poar long. Not he. He jest married a right rich girl! He! he!" And the old woman grinned at Ralph, and then at Mirandy, and then at the rest, until Ralph shuddered. Nothing was so frightful to him as to be fawned on by this grinning ogre, whose few lonesome, blackish teeth seemed ready to devour him. "He didn't stay poar, you bet a hoss!" and with this the coal was deposited on the pipe, and the lips began to crack like parchment as each puff of smoke escaped. "He married rich, you see," and here another significant look at the young master, and another fond look at Mirandy, as she puffed away reflectively. "His wife hadn't no book-larnin'. She'd been through the spellin'-book wunst, and had got as fur as 'asperity' on it a second time. But she couldn't read a word when she was married, and never could. She warn't overly smart. She hadn't hardly got the sense the law allows. But schools was skase in them air days, and, besides, book-larnin' don't do no good to a woman. Makes her stuck up. I never knowed but one gal in my life as had ciphered into fractions, and she was so dog-on stuck up that she turned up her nose one night at a apple-peelin' bekase I tuck a sheet off the bed to splice out the tablecloth, which was ruther short. And the sheet was mos' clean too. Had-n been slep on more'n wunst or twicet. But I was goin' fer to say that when Squire Hawkins married Virginny Gray he got a heap o' money, or, what's the same thing mostly, a heap o' good land. And that's better'n book-larnin', says I. Ef a gal had gone clean through all eddication, and got to the rule of three itself, that would-n buy a feather-bed. Squire Hawkins jest put eddication agin the gal's farm, and traded even, an' ef ary one of 'em got swindled, I never heerd no complaints."

And here she looked at Ralph in triumph, her hard face splintering into the hideous semblance of a smile. And Mirandy cast a blushing, gushing, all-imploring, and all-confiding look on the young master.

"I say, ole woman," broke in old Jack, "I say, wot is all this 'ere spoutin' about the Square fer?" and old Jack, having bit off an ounce of "pigtail," returned the plug to his pocket.

As for Ralph, he fell into a sort of terror. He had a guilty feeling that this speech of the old lady's had somehow committed him beyond recall to Mirandy. He did not see visions of breach-of-promise suits. But he trembled at the thought of an avenging big brother.

"Hanner, you kin come along, too, ef you're a mind, when you git the dishes washed," said Mrs. Means to the bound girl, as she shut and latched the back door. The Means family had built a new house in front of the old one, as a sort of advertisement of bettered circumstances, an eruption of shoddy feeling; but when the new building was completed, they found themselves unable to occupy it for anything else than a lumber room, and so, except a parlor which Mirandy had made an effort to furnish a little (in hope of the blissful time when somebody should "set up" with her of evenings), the new building was almost unoccupied, and the family went in and out through the back door, which, indeed, was the front door also, for, according to a curious custom, the "front" of the house was placed toward the south, though the "big road" (Hoosier for *highway*) ran along the northwest side, or, rather, past the northwest corner of it.

When the old woman had spoken thus to Hannah and had latched the door, she muttered, "That gal don't never show no gratitude fer favors;" to which Bud rejoined that he didn't think she had no great sight to be pertickler thankful fer. To which Mrs. Means made no reply, thinking it best, perhaps, not to wake up her dutiful son on so interesting a theme as her treatment of Hannah. Ralph felt glad that he was this evening to go to another boarding place. He should not hear the rest of the controversy.

Ralph walked to the school-house with Bill. They were friends again. For when Hank Banta's ducking and his dogged obstinacy in sitting in his wet clothes had brought on a serious fever, Ralph had called together the big boys, and had said: "We must take care of one another, boys.

Who will volunteer to take turns sitting up with Henry?"
He put his own name down, and all the rest followed.

"William Means and myself will sit up to-night," said
Ralph. And poor Bill had been from that moment the
teacher's friend. He was chosen to be Ralph's companion.
He was Puppy Means no longer! Hank could not be
conquered by kindness, and the teacher was made to feel
the bitterness of his resentment long after. But Bill
Means was for the time entirely placated, and he and
Ralph went to spelling-school together.

Every family furnished a candle. There were yellow
dips and white dips, burning, smoking, and flaring.
There was laughing, and talking, and giggling, and
simpering, and ogling, and flirting, and courting. What
a full-dress party is to Fifth Avenue, a spelling-school is
to Hoopole County. It is an occasion which is metaphor-
ically inscribed with this legend : "Choose your partners."
Spelling is only a blind in Hoopole County, as is dancing
on Fifth Avenue. But as there are some in society who
love dancing for its own sake, so in Flat Creek district
there were those who loved spelling for its own sake, and
who, smelling the battle from afar, had come to try their
skill in this tournament, hoping to freshen the laurels
they had won in their school days.

"I 'low," said Mr. Means, speaking as the principal
school trustee, "I 'low our friend the Square is jest the
man to boss this 'ere consarn to-night. Ef nobody ob-
jects, I'll app'int him. Come, Square, don't be bashful.
Walk up to the trough, fodder or no fodder, as the man
said to his donkey."

There was a general giggle at this, and many of the
young swains took occasion to nudge the girls alongside
them, ostensibly for the purpose of making them see the
joke, but really for the pure pleasure of nudging. The

Greeks figured Cupid as naked, probably because he wears so many disguises that they could not select a costume for him.

The Squire came to the front. Ralph made an inventory of the agglomeration which bore the name of Squire Hawkins, as follows:

1. A swallow-tail coat of indefinite age, worn only on state occasions, when its owner was called to figure in his public capacity. Either the Squire had grown too large or the coat too small.

2. A pair of black gloves, the most phenomenal, abnormal and unexpected apparition conceivable in Flat Creek district, where the preachers wore no coats in the summer, and where a black glove was never seen except on the hands of the Squire.

3. A wig of that dirty, waxen color so common to wigs. This one showed a continual inclination to slip off the owner's smooth, bald pate, and the Squire had frequently to adjust it. As his hair had been red, the wig did not accord with his face, and the hair ungrayed was doubly discordant with a countenance shriveled by age.

4. A semicircular row of whiskers hedging the edge of the jaw and chin. These were dyed a frightful dead-black, such a color as belonged to no natural hair or beard that ever existed. At the roots there was a quarter of an inch of white, giving the whiskers the appearance of having been stuck on.

5. A pair of spectacles "with tortoise-shell rim." Wont to slip off.

6. A glass eye, purchased of a peddler, and differing in color from its natural mate, perpetually getting out of focus by turning in or out.

7. A set of false teeth, badly fitted, and given to bobbing up and down.

8. The Squire proper, to whom these patches were loosely attached.

It is an old story that a boy wrote home to his father begging him to come West, because "mighty mean men get into office out here." But Ralph concluded that some Yankees had taught school in Hoopole County who would not have held a high place in the educational institutions of Massachusetts. Hawkins had some New England idioms, but they were well overlaid by a Western pronunciation.

"Ladies and gentlemen," he began, shoving up his spectacles, and sucking his lips over his white teeth to keep them in place, "ladies and gentlemen, young men and maidens, raley I'm obleeged to Mr. Means fer this honor," and the Squire took both hands and turned the top of his head round half an inch. Then he adjusted his spectacles. Whether he was obliged to Mr. Means for the honor of being compared to a donkey was not clear. "I feel in the inmost compartments of my animal spirits a most happifying sense of the success and futility of all my endeavors to sarve the people of Flat Creek deestrick, and the people of Tomkins township, in my weak way and manner." This burst of eloquence was delivered with a constrained air and an apparent sense of a danger that he, Squire Hawkins, might fall to pieces in his weak way and manner, and of the success and futility of all attempts at reconstruction. For by this time the ghastly pupil of the left eye, which was black, was looking away round to the left, while the little blue one on the right twinkled cheerfully toward the front. The front teeth would drop down so that the Squire's mouth was kept nearly closed, and his words whistled through.

"I feel as if I could be grandiloquent on this interesting occasion," twisting his scalp round, "but raley I must

forego any such exertions. It is spelling you want.
Spelling is the corner-stone, the grand, underlying sub-
terfuge, of a good eddication. I put the spellin'-book
prepared by the great Daniel Webster alongside the
Bible. I do, raley. I think I may put it ahead of the
Bible. Fer if it wurn't fer spellin'-books and sich occasions as these, where would the Bible be? I should like
to know. The man who got up, who compounded this
work of inextricable valoo was a benufactor to the whole
human race or any other." Here the spectacles fell off.
The Squire replaced them in some confusion, gave the
top of his head another twist, and felt of his glass eye,
while poor Shocky stared in wonder, and Betsey Short
rolled from side to side in the effort to suppress her
giggle. Mrs. Means and the other old ladies looked the
applause they could not speak.

"I app'int Larkin Lanham and Jeems Buchanan fer
captings," said the Squire. And the two young men thus
named took a stick and tossed it from hand to hand to
decide which should have the "first choice." One tossed
the stick to the other, who held it fast just where he happened to catch it. Then the first placed his hand above
the second, and so the hands were alternately changed to
the top. The one who held the stick last without room for
the other to take hold had gained the lot. This was tried
three times. As Larkin held the stick twice out of three
times, he had the choice. He hesitated a moment. Everybody looked toward tall Jim Phillips. But Larkin was
fond of a venture on unknown seas, and so he said, "I
take the master," while a buzz of surprise ran round the
room, and the captain of the other side, as if afraid his
opponent would withdraw the choice, retorted quickly,
and with a little smack of exultation and defiance in his
voice, "And *I* take Jeems Phillips."

And soon all present, except a few of the old folks, found themselves ranged in opposing hosts, the poor spellers lagging in, with what grace they could, at the foot of the two divisions. The Squire opened his spelling-book and began to give out the words to the two captains, who stood up and spelled against each other. It was not long until Larkin spelled "really" with one *l*, and had to sit down in confusion, while a murmur of satisfaction ran through the ranks of the opposing forces. His own side bit their lips. The slender figure of the young teacher took the place of the fallen leader, and the excitement made the house very quiet. Ralph dreaded the loss of prestige he would suffer if he should be easily spelled down. And at the moment of rising he saw in the darkest corner the figure of a well-dressed young man sitting in the shadow. Why should his evil genius haunt him? But by a strong effort he turned his attention away from Dr. Small, and listened carefully to the words which the Squire did not pronounce very distinctly, spelling them with extreme deliberation. This gave him an air of hesitation which disappointed those on his own side. They wanted him to spell with a dashing assurance. But he did not begin a word until he had mentally felt his way through it. After ten minutes of spelling hard words Jeems Buchanan, the captain on the other side, spelled "atrocious" with an *s* instead of a *c,* and subsided, his first choice, Jeems Phillips, coming up against the teacher. This brought the excitement to fever-heat. For though Ralph was chosen first, it was entirely on trust, and most of the company were disappointed. The champion who now stood up against the school-master was a famous speller.

Jim Phillips was a tall, lank, stoop-shouldered fellow who had never distinguished himself in any other pursuit

than spelling. Except in this one art of spelling he was
of no account. He could not catch well or bat well in ball.
He could not throw well enough to make his mark in
that famous Western game of bull-pen. He did not succeed well in any study but that of Webster's Elementary.
But in that he was—to use the usual Flat Creek locution
—in that he was "a hoss." This genius for spelling is in
some people a sixth sense, a matter of intuition. Some
spellers are born, and not made, and their facility reminds
one of the mathematical prodigies that crop out every
now and then to bewilder the world. Bud Means, fore-
seeing that Ralph would be pitted against Jim Phillips,
had warned his friend that Jim could "spell like thunder
and lightning," and that it "took a powerful smart speller" to beat him, for he knew "a heap of spelling-book."
To have "spelled down the master" is next thing to having whipped the biggest bully in Hoopole County, and
Jim had "spelled down" the last three masters. He divided the hero-worship of the district with Bud Means.

For half an hour the Squire gave out hard words.
What a blessed thing our crooked orthography is! Without it there could be no spelling-schools. As Ralph discovered his opponent's metal he became more and more
cautious. He was now satisfied that Jim would eventually beat him. The fellow evidently knew more about the
spelling-book than old Noah Webster himself. As he
stood there, with his dull face and long, sharp nose, his
hands behind his back, and his voice spelling infallibly,
it seemed to Hartsook that his superiority must lie in his
nose. Ralph's cautiousness answered a double purpose;
it enabled him to tread surely, and it was mistaken by
Jim for weakness. Phillips was now confident that he
should carry off the scalp of the fourth school-master before the evening was over. He spelled eagerly, confi-

dently, brilliantly. Stoop-shouldered as he was, he began to straighten up. In the minds of all the company the odds were in his favor. He saw this, and became ambitious to distinguish himself by spelling without giving the matter any thought.

Ralph always believed that he would have been speedily defeated by Phillips had it not been for two thoughts which braced him. The sinister shadow of young Dr. Small sitting in the dark corner by the water-bucket nerved him. A victory over Phillips was a defeat to one who wished only ill to the young school-master. The other thought that kept his pluck alive was the recollection of Bull. He approached a word as Bull approached the raccoon. He did not take hold until he was sure of his game. When he took hold, it was with a quiet assurance of success. As Ralph spelled in this dogged way for half an hour the hardest words the Squire could find, the excitement steadily rose in all parts of the house, and Ralph's friends even ventured to whisper that "maybe Jim had cotched his match, after all!"

But Phillips never doubted of his success.

"Theodolite," said the Squire.

"T-h-e, the, o-d, od, theod, o, theodo, l-y-t-e, the-odolite," spelled the champion.

"Next," said the Squire, nearly losing his teeth in his excitement. Ralph spelled the word slowly and correctly, and the conquered champion sat down in confusion. The excitement was so great for some minutes that the spelling was suspended. Everybody in the house had shown sympathy with one or the other of the combatants, except the silent shadow in the corner. It had not moved during the contest, and did not show any interest now in the result.

"Gewhilliky crickets! Thunder and lightning! Licked

him all to smash!" said Bud, rubbing his hands on his knees. "That beats my time all holler!"

And Betsey Short giggled until her tuck-comb fell out, though she was not on the defeated side.

Shocky got up and danced with pleasure.

But one suffocating look from the aqueous eyes of Mirandy destroyed the last spark of Ralph's pleasure in his triumph, and sent that awful below-zero feeling all through him.

"He's powerful smart, is the master," said old Jack to Mr. Pete Jones. "He'll beat the whole kit and tuck of 'em afore he's through. I know'd he was smart. That's the reason I tuck him," proceeded Mr. Means.

"Yaas, but he don't lick enough. Not nigh," answered Pete Jones. "No lickin', no larnin'," says I.

It was now not so hard. The other spellers on the opposite side went down quickly under the hard words which the Squire gave out. The master had mowed down all but a few, his opponents had given up the battle, and all had lost their keen interest in a contest to which there could be but one conclusion, for there were only the poor spellers left. But Ralph Hartsook ran against a stump where he was least expecting it. It was the Squire's custom, when one of the smaller scholars or poorer spellers rose to spell against the master, to give out eight or ten easy words, that they might have some breathing-spell before being slaughtered, and then to give a poser or two which soon settled them. He let them run a little, as a cat does a doomed mouse. There was now but one person left on the opposite side, and, as she rose in her blue calico dress, Ralph recognized Hannah, the bound girl at old Jack Means's. She had not attended school in the district, and had never spelled in spelling-school before, and was chosen last as an uncertain quantity. The

Squire began with easy words of two syllables, from that page of Webster, so well known to all who ever thumbed it, as "baker," from the word that stands at the top of the page. She spelled these words in an absent and uninterested manner. As everybody knew that she would have to go down as soon as this preliminary skirmishing was over, everybody began to get ready to go home, and already there was the buzz of preparation. Young men were timidly asking girls if "they could see them safe home," which was the approved formula, and were trembling in mortal fear of "the mitten." Presently the Squire, thinking it time to close the contest, pulled his scalp forward, adjusted his glass eye, which had been examining his nose long enough, and turned over the leaves of the book to the great words at the place known to spellers as "incomprehensibility," and began to give out those "words of eight syllables with the accent on the sixth." Listless scholars now turned round, and ceased to whisper, in order to be in at the master's final triumph. But to their surprise "ole Miss Meanses' white nigger," as some of them called her in allusion to her slavish life, spelled these great words with as perfect ease as the master. Still not doubting the result, the Squire turned from place to place and selected all the hard words he could find. The school became utterly quiet, the excitement was too great for the ordinary buzz. Would "Meanses' Hanner" beat the master? beat the master that had laid out Jim Phillips? Everybody's sympathy was now turned to Hannah. Ralph noticed that even Shocky had deserted him, and that his face grew brilliant every time Hannah spelled a word. In fact, Ralph deserted himself. As he saw the fine, timid face of the girl so long oppressed flush and shine with interest; as he looked at the rather low but broad and intelligent brow and the fresh, white complexion and saw the rich, womanly nature coming to the surface under the influence of applause and sympathy—he did not want to beat. If he had not felt that a victory given would insult her, he would have missed intentionally. The bulldog, the stern, relentless setting of the will, had gone, he knew not whither. And there had come in its place, as he looked in that face, a something which he did not understand. You did not, gentle reader, the first time it came to you.

The Squire was puzzled. He had given out all the hard words in the book. He again pulled the top of his head forward. Then he wiped his spectacles and put them on. Then out of the depths of his pocket he fished up a list of words just coming into use in those days—words not in the spelling-book. He regarded the paper attentively with his blue right eye. His black left eye meanwhile fixed itself in such a stare on Mirandy Means that she shuddered and hid her eyes in her red silk handkerchief.

"Daguerreotype," sniffed the Squire. It was Ralph's turn.

"D-a-u, dau—"

"Next."

And Hannah spelled it right.

Such a buzz followed that Betsey Short's giggle could not be heard, but Shocky shouted: "Hanner beat! my Hanner spelled down the master!" And Ralph went over and congratulated her.

And Dr. Small sat perfectly still in the corner.

And then the Squire called them to order, and said: "As our friend Hanner Thomson is the only one left on her side, she will have to spell against nearly all on t'other side. I shall therefore take the liberty of procrastinating the completion of this interesting and exacting contest until to-morrow evening. I hope our friend Hanner may

again carry off the cypress crown of glory. There is
nothing better for us than healthful and kindly simula-
tion."

Dr. Small, who knew the road to practice, escorted
Mirandy, and Bud went home with somebody else. The
others of the Means family hurried on, while Hannah,
the champion, stayed behind a minute to speak to Shocky.
Perhaps it was because Ralph saw that Hannah must go
alone that he suddenly remembered having left something
which was of no consequence, and resolved to go round
by Mr. Means's and get it.

## MYOPIA

### BY WALLACE RICE

As down the street he took his stroll,
   He cursed, for all he is a saint.
He saw a sign atop a pole,
As down the street he took a stroll,
And climbed it up (near-sighted soul),
   So he could read—and read "FRESH
      PAINT,"  . . .
As down the street he took a stroll,
   He cursed, for all he is a saint.

# ANATOLE DUBOIS AT DE HORSE SHOW

## BY WALLACE BRUCE AMSBARY

My vife an' me ve read so moch
  In papier here of late,
About Chicago Horse Show, ve
  Remember day an' date.
Ve mak' it op togedder dat
  Ve go an' see dat show,
Dere's som't'ing dere ve fin' it out
  Maybe ve vant to know.

Ve leave de leddle farm avile,
  Dat's near to Bourbonnais;
Ve're soon op to Chicago town
  For spen' de night an' day;
I nevere lak' dat busy place,
  It's mos' too swif' for me,—
Ve vaste no tam', but gat to place
  Dat ve is com' for see.

Ve pay de price for tak' us in,
  Dey geeve me *deux* ticquette;
Charlotte an' me ve com' for see
  De Horse Show now, you bet.
Ve soon gat in it veree moch,
  "De push," I t'ink you call,
To inside on de beeg building,
  Ve're going to see it all.

De Coliseum is de place,
　　Dey mak' de Horse Show dere,
Five tam's so beeg dan any barn
　　At Bourbonnais, by gar!
I'm look aroun' for place dey haf'
　　For dem to pitch de hay.
"I guess it's 'out of sight,' I t'ink,"
　　Dey's von man to me say.

An' den ve valk aroun' an' 'roun'
　　Som' horses for to see;
Dere's pretty vomans, lots of dem,
　　But, for de life of me,
I can not see de trotter nag,
　　Or vat's called t'oroughbred,
I vonder if ve mak' mistake,
　　Gat in wrong place instead.

But Charlotte is not disappoint',
　　Her eyes dey shine so bright,
It's ven she sees dem vimmens folks,
　　Dey dance vit moch delight;
I den vos tak' a look myself
　　On ladies vit fin' drass,
Dere's nodding else in dat whol' place
　　Dat is so interes'.

I say, "Charlotte," say I to her,
　　"Dat ladee in box seat—
Across de vay vos von beeg swell,
　　Her beauty's hard to beat;
De von dat's gat fon*ee* eyeglass
　　Opon a leddle stek,
I'm t'ink she is most' fin' loo*kin'*
　　W'en she bow an' spe'k.

"It's pretty drass dat she's got on,
   I lak' de polonaise,
Vere bodice it is all meex op
   Vit jabot all de vays.
Dat's hang in front vit pleats all roun'—
   It is von fin' tableau."
An' den Charlotte she turn to me
   An' ask me how I know

So moch about de Beeg Horse Show,
   W'ich we are com' for see;
An' den I op an' tol' her dere
   Dat I had com' to be
Expert on informatione,
   Read papier, I fin' out
Vat all is in de Horse's Show,
   An' vat's it all about.

I point to ladee in nex' box,
   She's feex op mighty vell,
I vish I could haf' vords enough
   Vat she had on to tell;
De firs' part it vas nodding moch,
   From cloth it vas quite free,
Lak' fleur-de-lis at Easter tam',
   Mos' beautiful to see.

An' den dere is commence a line
   Of fluffy cream soufflé,
My vife it mak' her very diz',
   She's not a vord to say.
An' den com' yard of *crêpe de chine,*
   Vit omelette stripe beneadt',
All fill it op vit fine guimpe jew'ls
   An' concertina pleat.

Mon Dieu! an' who vould evere t'ink
  Dat Horse Show vas lak' dese!
A Horse Show dere vidout no horse,
  I t'ink dat's strange beez*nesse*.
But I suppose affer de man
  De dry-goods bill dey pay,
Dere's nodding lef' to spen' on horse
  Ontil som' odder day.

I tell you every hour you leeve,
  You fin' out som't'ing new;
An' now I haf' som' vords to tell,
  Som' good it might do you;
It's mighty fonny, de advise
  I'm geeve to you, of course,
But never go to Horses Show
  Expecting to see horse.

# THE CHAMPION CHECKER-PLAYER OF AMERIKY

BY JAMES WHITCOMB RILEY

Of course as fur as Checker-playin's concerned, you can't jest adzackly claim 'at lots makes fortunes and lots gits bu'sted at it—but still, it's on'y simple jestice to acknowledge 'at there're absolute p'ints in the game 'at takes scientific principles to figger out, and a mighty level-headed feller to *dimo*nstrate, don't you understand!

Checkers is a' *old* enough game, ef age is any rickommendation; and it's a' evident fact, too, 'at "the tooth of time," as the feller says, which fer the last six thousand years has gained some reputation fer a-eatin' up things in giner'l, don't 'pear to 'a' gnawed much of a hole in Checkers—jedgin' from the checker-board of to-day and the ones 'at they're uccasionally shovellin' out at *Pomp'y-i,* er whatever its name is. Turned up a checker-board there not long ago, I wuz readin' 'bout, 'at still had the spots on—as plain and fresh as the modern white-pine board o' our'n, squared off with pencil-marks and pokeberry-juice. These is facts 'at history herself has dug out, and of course it ain't fer me ner you to turn our nose up at Checkers, whuther we ever tamper with the fool-game er not. Fur's that's concerned, I don't p'tend to be no checker-player *myse'f,*—but I know'd a feller onc't 'at *could* play, and sorto' made a business of it; and *that* man, in my opinion, was a geenyus! Name wuz Wesley Cotterl—John Wesley Cotterl—jest plain Wes, as us fellers round the Shoe-Shop ust to call him; ust to allus make the Shoe-Shop his headquarters-like; and, rain er shine, wet er dry, you'd allus find *Wes* on hands, ready to banter some feller fer a game, er jest a-settin' humped up there over the checker-board all alone, a-cipher'n' out some new move er 'nuther, and whistlin' low and solem' to hisse'f-like and a-payin' no attention to nobody.

And *I'll* tell *you*, Wes Cotterl wuz no man's fool, as sly as you keep it! He wuz a deep thinker, Wes wuz; and ef, he'd 'a' jest turned that mind o' his loose on *preachin'*, fer instunce, and the 'terpertation o' the Bible, don't you know, Wes 'ud 'a' worked p'ints out o' there 'at no livin' expounderers ever got in gunshot of!

But Wes he didn't 'pear to be cut out fer nothin' much but jest Checker-playin'. Oh, of course, he *could* knock round his own woodpile some, and garden a little, more er less; and the neighbers ust to find Wes purty handy 'bout trimmin' fruit-trees, you understand, and workin' 'n among the worms and cattapillers in the vines and shrubbery, and the like. And handlin' bees!—They wuzn't no man under the heavens 'at knowed more 'bout handlin' bees'n Wes Cotterl!—"Settlin'" the blame' things when they wuz a-swarmin'; and a-robbin' hives, and all sich fool-resks. W'y, I've saw Wes Cotterl, 'fore now, when a swarm of bees 'ud settle in a' orchard,—like they will sometimes, you know,—I've saw Wes Cotterl jest roll up his shirt-sleeves and bend down a' apple tree limb 'at wuz jest kivvered with the pesky things, and scrape 'em back into the hive with his naked hands, by the quart and gallon, and never git a scratch! You couldn't *hire* a bee to sting Wes Cotterl! But *lazy?*—I think that man had railly ort to 'a' been a' Injun! He wuz the fust and on'y man 'at ever I laid eyes on 'at wuz too lazy to drap a checker-man to p'int out the right road fer a feller 'at ast him onc't the way to Burke's Mill; and Wes, 'ithout ever a-liftin' eye er finger, jest sorto' crooked out that mouth o' his'n in the direction the feller wanted, and says: *"H-yonder!"* and went on with his whistlin'. But all this hain't Checkers, and that's what I started out to tell ye.

Wes had a way o' jest natchurly a-cleanin' out anybody and ever'body 'at 'ud he'p hold up a checker-board! Wes wuzn't what you'd call a *lively* player at all, ner a competiter 'at talked much 'crost the board er made much furse over a game whilse he *wuz* a-playin'. He had his faults, o' course, and *would* take back moves 'casion'ly, er inch up on you ef you didn't watch him, mebby. But, *as a rule,* Wes had the insight to grasp the idy of whoever wuz a-playin' ag'in' him, and *his* style o' game, you understand, and wuz on the lookout continual'; and under sich circumstances *could* play as *honest* a game o' Checkers as the babe unborn.

One thing in *Wes's* favor allus wuz the feller's temper. —Nothin' 'peared to aggervate Wes, and nothin' on earth could break his slow and lazy way o' takin' his own time fer ever'thing. You jest *couldn't crowd Wes* er git him rattled anyway.—Jest 'peared to have one fixed principle, and that wuz to take plenty o' time, and never make no move 'ithout a-ciphern'n' ahead on the prob'ble consequences, don't you understand! "Be shore you're right," Wes 'ud say, a-lettin' up fer a second on that low and sorry-like little wind-through-the-keyhole whistle o' his, and a-nosin' out a place whur he could swap one man fer two.—"Be shore you're right"—and somep'n' after this style wuz Wes's way: "Be shore you're right"—(whistling a long, lonesome bar of "Barbara Allen")—"and then"—(another long, retarded bar)—"go ahead!"—and by the time the feller 'ud git through with his whistlin', and a-stoppin' and a-startin' in ag'in, he'd be about three men ahead to your one. And then he'd jest go on with his whistlin' 'sef nothin' had happened, and mebby you a-jest a-rearin' and a-callin' him all the mean, outlandish, ornry names 'at you could lay tongue to.

But Wes's good nature, I reckon, was the thing 'at he'ped him out as much as any other p'ints the feller had. And *Wes 'ud allus win, in the long run!*—I don't keer *who* played ag'inst him! It was on'y a question o' time with Wes o' waxin' it to the best of 'em. Lots o' players has *tackled* Wes, and right at the *start* 'ud mebby give him trouble,—but in the *long run,* now mind ye—*in the long run,* no mortal man, I reckon, had any business o' rubbin' knees with Wes Cotterl under no airthly checker-board in all this vale o' tears!

I mind onc't th' come along a high-toned feller from in around In'i'nop'lus somers.—Wuz a *lawyer,* er some *p'fessional* kind o' man. Had a big yaller, luther-kivvered book under his arm, and a bunch o' these-'ere big en-*velop*'s and a lot o' suppeenies stickin' out o' his breast-pocket. Mighty slick-lookin' feller he wuz; wore a stove-pipe hat, sorto' set 'way back on his head—so's to show off his Giner'l Jackson forr'ed, don't you know! Well-sir, this feller struck the place, on some business er other, and then missed the hack 'at *ort* to 'a' tuk him out o' here sooner'n it *did* take him out!—And whilse he wuz a-loaf-in' round, sorto' lonesome—like a feller allus *is* in a strange place, you know—he kindo' drapped in on our crowd at the Shoe-Shop, ostenchably to git a boot-strop stitched on, but *I* knowed, the minute he set foot in the door, 'at *that* feller wanted *comp'ny* wuss'n *cobblin'.*

Well, as good luck would have it, there set Wes, as usual, with the checker-board in his lap, a-playin' all by hisse'f, and a-whistlin' so low and solem'-like and sad it railly made the crowd seem like a *religious* getherun' o' some kind er other, we wuz all so quiet and still-like, as the man come in.

Well, the stranger stated his business, set down, tuk off his boot, and set there nussin' his foot and talkin' weather fer ten minutes, I reckon, 'fore he ever 'peared to notice Wes at all. We wuz all back'ard, anyhow, 'bout talkin' much; besides, we knowed, long afore he come in, all about how hot the weather wuz, and the pore chance there wuz o' rain, and all that; and so the subject had purty well died out, when jest then the feller's eyes struck Wes and the checker-board,—and I'll never fergit the warm, salvation smile 'at flashed over him at the promisin' discovery. *"What!"* says he, a-grinnin' like a' angel and a-edgin' his cheer to'rds Wes, "have we a checker-board and checkers here?"

"We hev," says I, knowin' 'at Wes wouldn't let go o' that whistle long enough to answer—more'n to mebby nod his head.

"And who is your best player?" says the feller, kindo' pitiful-like, with another inquirin' look at Wes.

"Him," says I, a-pokin' Wes with a peg-float. But Wes on'y spit kindo' absent-like, and went on with his whistlin'.

"Much of a player, is he?" says the feller, with a sorto' doubtful smile at Wes ag'in.

"Plays a purty good hick'ry," says I, a-pokin' Wes ag'in. "Wes," says I, "here's a gentleman 'at 'ud mebby like to take a hand with you there, and give you a few idys," says I.

"Yes," says the stranger, eager-like, a-settin' his plug-hat keerful' up in the empty shelvin', and a-rubbin' his hands and smilin' as confident-like as old Hoyle hisse'f,— "Yes, indeed, I'd be glad to give the gentleman" (meanin' Wes) "a' idy er two about Checkers—ef *he'd* jest as lief,

—'cause I reckon ef there're any one thing 'at I *do* know more about 'an another, it's Checkers," says he; "and there're no game 'at delights me more—*pervidin'*, o' course, I find a competiter 'at kin make it anyways inte*rest*in'."

"Got much of a rickord on Checkers?" says I.

"Well," says the feller, "I don't like to brag, but I've never *ben* beat—in any *legitimut* contest," says he, "and I've played more'n one o' *them*," he says, "here and there round the country. Of course, *your friend* here," he went on, smilin' sociable at Wes, *"he'll* take it all in good part ef I should happen to lead him a little—jest as *I'd* do," he says, "ef it wuz possible fer him to lead *me*."

*"Wes,"* says I, *"has* warmed the wax in the yeers of some mighty good checker-players," says I, as he squared the board around, still a-whistlin' to hisse'f-like, as the stranger tuk his place, a-smilin'-like and roachin' back his hair.

"Move," says Wes.

"No," says the feller, with a polite flourish of his hand; "the first move shall be your'n." And, by jucks! fer all he wouldn't take even the advantage of a starter, he flaxed it to Wes the fust game in less'n fifteen minutes.

"Right shore you've give' me your best player?" he says, smilin' round at the crowd, as Wes set squarin' the board fer another game and whistlin' as onconcerned-like as ef nothin' had happened more'n ordinary.

" 'S your move," says Wes, a-squintin' out into the game 'bout forty foot from shore, and a-whistlin' purt' nigh in a whisper.

Well-sir, it 'peared-like the feller railly didn't *try* to play; and you could see, too, 'at Wes knowed he'd about met his match, and played accordin'. He didn't make no move at all 'at he didn't give keerful thought to; whilse the feller——! well, as I wuz sayin', it jest 'peared-like *Checkers* wuz *child's-play* fer him! Putt in most o' the time 'long through the game a-sayin' things calkilated to kindo' bore a' ordinary man. But Wes helt hisse'f purty level, and didn't show no signs, and kep' up his *whistlin'*, mighty well——considerin'.

"Reckon you play the *fiddle, too*, as well as *Checkers?*" says the feller, laughin', as Wes come a-whistlin' out of the little end of the second game and went on a-fixin' fer the next round.

"''S my move!" says Wes, 'thout seemin' to notice the feller's tantalizin' words whatsomever.

"''L! *this* time," thinks I, "Mr. Smarty from the *me*trolopin deestricts, *you're* liable to git *waxed——shore!*" But the *feller* didn't 'pear to think so at all, and played right ahead as glib-like and keerless as ever——'casion'ly a-throwin' in them sircastic remarks o' his'n,——'bout bein' "slow and shore" 'bout things in gineral——"Liked to *see* that," he said:——"Liked to see fellers do things with plenty o' *deliberation,* and even ef a feller *wuzn't* much of a checker-player, liked to see him *die* slow *anyhow!*—— and then 'tend his own funeral," he says,——"and march in the p'session——to his own *music,*" says he.——And jest then his remarks wuz brung to a close by Wes a-jumpin' two men, and a-lightin' square in the king-row. . . . "Crown that," says Wes, a-droppin' back into his old tune. And fer the rest o' *that* game Wes helt the feller purty level, but had to finally knock under——but by jest the clos'test kind o' shave o' winnin'.

"They ain't much use," says the feller, "o' keepin' *this* thing up——'less I could manage, *some* way er other, to git beat *onc't 'n a while!*"

"Move," says Wes, a-drappin' back into the same old whistle and a-*settlin'* there.

" 'Music has charms,' as the Good Book tells us," says the feller, kindo' nervous-like, and a-roachin' his hair back as ef some sort o' p'tracted headache wuz a-settin' in.

"Never wuz *'skunked,'* wuz ye?" says Wes, kindo' sudduent-like, with a fur-off look in them big white eyes o' his —and then a-whistlin' right on 'sef he hadn't said *nothin'*.

*"Not much!"* says the feller, sorto' s'prised-like, as ef such a' idy as that had never struck him afore.—"Never was 'skunked' *myse'f:* but I've saw fellers in my time 'at *wuz!"* says he.

But from that time on I noticed the feller 'peared to play more keerful, and railly la'nched into the game with somepin' like inter'st. Wes he seemed to be jest a-limberin'-up-like; and-sir, blame me! ef he didn't walk the feller's log fer him *that* time, 'thout no 'pearent trouble at all!

"And, *now,"* says Wes, all quiet-like, a-squarin' the board fer another'n,—"we're kindo' gittin' at things *right.* Move." And away went that little unconcerned whistle o' his ag'in, and *Mr. Cityman* jest gittin' white and sweaty too—he wuz so nervous. Ner he didn't 'pear to find much to laugh at in the *next* game—ner the next *two* games nuther! Things wuz a-gettin' mighty inter*est*in' 'bout them times, and I guess the feller wuz ser'ous-like a-wakin' up to the solem' fact 'at it tuk 'bout all *his* spare time to keep up his end o' the row, and even that state o' pore satisfaction wuz a-creepin' furder and furder away from him ever' new turn he undertook. Whilse *Wes* jest 'peared to git more deliber't' and certain ever' game; and that unendin' se'f-satisfied and comfortin' little whistle o' his never drapped a stitch, but toed out ever' game alike, —to'rds the *last,* and, fer the *most* part, disasterss to the feller 'at had started in with sich confi*dence* and actchul promise, don't you know.

Well-sir, the feller stuck the whole *forenoon* out, and then the *afternoon;* and then knuckled down to it 'way into the night—yes, and plum *midnight!*—And he buckled into the thing bright and airly *next morning!* And-sir, fer *two long days* and nights, a-hardly a-stoppin' long enough to *eat,* the feller stuck it out,—and Wes a-jest a-warpin' it to him hand-over-fist, and leavin' him furder behind, ever' game!—till finally, to'rds the last, the feller got so blamedon worked up and excited-like, he jes' 'peared actchully purt' nigh plum crazy and histurical as a woman!

It was a-gittin' late into the shank of the second day, and the boys hed jest lit a candle fer 'em to finish out one of the clost'est games the feller'd played Wes fer some time. But Wes wuz jest as cool and ca'm as ever, and still a-whistlin' consolin' to hisse'f-like, whilse the feller jest 'peared wore out and ready to drap right in his tracks any minute.

*"Durn you!"* he snarled out at Wes, "hain't you never goern to move?" And there set Wes, a-balancin' a check-er-man above the board, a-studyin' whur to set it, and a-fillin' in the time with that-air whistle.

*"Flames and flashes!"* says the feller ag'in, "will you *ever* stop that death-seducin' tune o' your'n long enough to move?"—And as Wes deliber't'ly set his man down whur the feller see he'd haf to jump it and lose two men and a king, Wes wuz a-singin', low and sad-like, as ef all to hisse'f:

> "O we'll move that man, and leave him there.—
> Fer the love of B-a-r-b—bry Al-len!"

Well-sir! the feller jest jumped to his feet, upset the board, and tore out o' the shop stark-starin' crazy—blame ef he wuzn't!—'cause some of us putt out after him and overtook him 'way beyent the 'pike-bridge, and hollered to him;—and he shuk his fist at us and hollered back and says, says he: "Ef you fellers over here," says he, " 'll agree to *muzzle* that durn checker-player o' your'n, I'll bet fifteen hunderd dollars to fifteen cents 'at I kin beat him 'leven games out of ever' dozent!—But there're *no money*," he says, " 'at kin hire me to piay him ag'in, on this aboundin' airth, on'y on them conditions—'cause that durn, eternal, infernal, dad-blasted whistle o' his 'ud beat the oldest man in Ameriky!"

# DARBY AND JOAN

BY ST. JOHN HONEYWOOD

## I

When Darby saw the setting sun,
He swung his scythe, and home he run,
Sat down, drank off his quart, and said,
"My work is done, I'll go to bed."
"My work is done!" retorted Joan,
"My work is done! your constant tone;
But hapless woman ne'er can say,
'My work is done,' till judgment day.
You men can sleep all night, but we
Must toil."—"Whose fault is that?" quoth he.
"I know your meaning," Joan replied,
"But, Sir, my tongue shall not be tied;
I will go on, and let you know
What work poor women have to do:
First, in the morning, though we feel
As sick as drunkards when they reel;
Yes, feel such pains in back and head
As would confine you men to bed,
We ply the brush, we wield the broom,
We air the beds, and right the room;
The cows must next be milked—and then
We get the breakfast for the men.
Ere this is done, with whimpering cries,
And bristly hair, the children rise;

166

These must be dressed, and dosed with rue,
And fed—and all because of you:
We next"— Here Darby scratched his head,
And stole off grumbling to his bed;
And only said, as on she run,
"Zounds! woman's clack is never done."


## II


At early dawn, ere Phœbus rose,
Old Joan resumed her tale of woes;
When Darby thus—"I'll end the strife,
Be you the man and I the wife:
Take you the scythe and mow, while I
Will all your boasted cares supply."
"Content," quoth Joan, "give me my stint."
This Darby did, and out she went.
Old Darby rose and seized the broom,
And whirled the dirt about the room:
Which having done, he scarce knew how,
He hied to milk the brindled cow.
The brindled cow whisked round her tail
In Darby's eyes, and kicked the pail.
The clown, perplexed with grief and pain,
Swore he'd ne'er try to milk again:
When turning round, in sad amaze,
He saw his cottage in a blaze:
For as he chanced to brush the room,
In careless haste, he fired the broom.
The fire at last subdued, he swore
The broom and he would meet no more.
Pressed by misfortune, and perplexed,
Darby prepared for breakfast next;

But what to get he scarcely knew—
The bread was spent, the butter too.
His hands bedaubed with paste and flour,
Old Darby labored full an hour:
But, luckless wight! thou couldst not make
The bread take form of loaf or cake.
As every door wide open stood,
In pushed the sow in quest of food;
And, stumbling onward, with her snout
O'erset the churn—the cream ran out.
As Darby turned, the sow to beat,
The slippery cream betrayed his feet;
He caught the bread trough in his fall,
And down came Darby, trough, and all.
The children, wakened by the clatter,
Start up, and cry, "Oh! what's the matter?"
Old Jowler barked, and Tabby mewed,
And hapless Darby bawled aloud,
"Return, my Joan, as heretofore,
I'll play the housewife's part no more:
Since now, by sad experience taught,
Compared to thine my work is naught;
Henceforth, as business calls, I'll take,
Content, the plough, the scythe, the rake,
And never more transgress the line
Our fates have marked, while thou art mine.
Then, Joan, return, as heretofore,
I'll vex thy honest soul no more;
Let's each our proper task attend—
Forgive the past, and strive to mend."

# WHEN THE FROST IS ON THE PUNKIN

BY JAMES WHITCOMB RILEY

When the frost is on the punkin and the fodder's in the
    shock,
And you hear the kyouck and gobble of the struttin'
    turkey-cock,
And the clackin' of the guineys, and the cluckin' of the
    hens,
And the rooster's hallelooyer as he tiptoes on the fence,
Oh, it's then's the time a feller is a feelin' at his best,
With the risin' sun to greet him from a night of gracious
    rest,
As he leaves the house bareheaded and goes out to feed
    the stock,
When the frost is on the punkin and the fodder's in the
    shock.

There's sompin kind o' hearty-like about the atmosphere
When the heat of summer's over and the coolin' fall is
    here.
Of course we miss the flowers, and the blossoms on the
    trees,
And the mumble of the hummin'-birds and the buzzin' of
    the bees;
But the air's so appetizin', and the landscape through the
    haze
Of a crisp and sunny morning of the early autumn days
Is a picture that no painter has the colorin' to mock,
When the frost is on the punkin and the fodder's in the
    shock.

# WHEN THE FROST IS ON THE PUNKIN

The husky, rusty rustle of the tassels of the corn,
And the raspin' of the tangled leaves as golden as the
      morn;
The stubble in the furries—kind o' lonesome like, but still
A preachin' sermons to us of the barns they growed to fill;
The straw-stack in the medder, and the reaper in the shed,
The hosses in their stalls below, the clover overhead,—
Oh, it sets my heart a clickin' like the tickin' of a clock,
When the frost is on the punkin and the fodder's in the
      shock.

# LAFFING

BY JOSH BILLINGS

Anatomikally konsidered, laffing iz the sensation ov pheeling good all over, and showing it principally in one spot.

Morally konsidered, it iz the next best thing tew the 10 commandments.  .  .  .

Theoretikally konsidered, it kan out-argy all the logik in existence.  .  .  .

Pyroteknikally konsidered, it is the fire-works of the soul.  .  .  .

But i don't intend this essa for laffing in the lump, but for laffing on the half-shell.

Laffing iz just az natral tew cum tew the surface az a rat iz tew cum out ov hiz hole when he wants tew.

Yu kant keep it back by swallowing enny more than yu kan the heekups.

If a man *kan't* laff there iz sum mistake made in putting him together, and if he *won't* laff he wants az mutch keeping away from az a bear-trap when it iz sot.

I have seen people who laffed altogether too mutch for their own good or for ennyboddy else's; they laft like a barrell ov nu sider with the tap pulled out, a perfekt stream.

This is a grate waste ov natral juice.

I have seen other people who didn't laff enuff tew giv themselfs vent; they waz like a barrell ov nu sider too, that waz bunged up tite, apt tew start a hoop and leak all away on the sly.

Thare ain't neither ov theze 2 ways right, and they never ought tew be pattented. . . .

Genuine laffing iz the vent ov the soul, the nostrils of the heart, and iz just az necessary for health and happiness az spring water iz for a trout.

Thare iz one kind ov a laff that i always did rekommend; it looks out ov the eye fust with a merry twinkle, then it kreeps down on its hands and kneze and plays around the mouth like a pretty moth around the blaze ov a kandle, then it steals over into the dimples ov the cheeks and rides around into thoze little whirlpools for a while, then it lites up the whole face like the mello bloom on a damask roze, then it swims oph on the air with a peal az klear and az happy az a dinner-bell, then it goes bak agin on golden tiptoze like an angel out for an airing, and laze down on its little bed ov violets in the heart where it cum from.

Thare iz another laff that nobody kan withstand; it iz just az honest and noisy az a distrikt skool let out tew play, it shakes a man up from hiz toze tew hiz temples, it dubbles and twists him like a whiskee phit, it lifts him oph from his cheer, like feathers, and lets him bak agin like melted led, it goes all thru him like a pikpocket, and finally leaves him az weak and az krazy az tho he had bin soaking all day in a Rushing bath and forgot to be took out.

This kind ov a laff belongs tew jolly good phellows who are az healthy az quakers, and who are az eazy tew pleaze az a gall who iz going tew be married to-morrow.

In konklushion i say laff every good chance yu kan git, but don't laff unless yu feal like it, for there ain't nothing in this world more harty than a good honest laff, nor nothing more hollow than a hartless one.

When yu do laff open yure mouth wide enuff for the

noize tew git out without squealing, thro yure hed bak az tho yu waz going tew be shaved, hold on tew yure false hair with both hands and then laff till yure soul gets thoroly rested.

But i shall tell yu more about theze things at sum fewter time.

# GRIZZLY-GRU

BY IRONQUILL

O Thoughts of the past and present,
O whither, and whence, and where,
    Demanded my soul, as I scaled the height
    Of the pine-clad peak in the somber night,
In the terebinthine air.

While pondering on the frailty
Of happiness, hope, and mirth,
    The ascending sun with derisive scoff
    Hurled its golden lances and smote me off
From the bulge of the restless earth.

Through the yellowish dawn of velvet
Where stars were so thickly strewn,
    That quietly chuckled as I passed through,
    I fell in the gardens of Grizzly-Gru,
On the mad, mysterious moon.

I fell on the turquoise ether,
Low down in the wondrous west,
    And thence to the moon in whose yielding blue
    Were hidden the gardens of Grizzly-Gru,
In the Monarchy of Unrest.

And there were the fairy gardens,
Where beautiful cherubs grew
    In daintiest way and on separate stalks,
    In the listed rows by the jasper walks,
Near the palace of Grizzly-Gru.

While strolling around the garden
I noticed the rows were full
  Of every conceivable size and type—
  Some that were buds, and some nearly ripe,
And some that were ready to pull.

In gauzy and white corolla,
Was one who had eyes of blue,
  A little excuse of a baby nose,
  Little pink ears, and ten little toes,
And a mouth that kept saying ah-goo.

Ah-gooing as I came near her,
She raised up her arms in glee—
  Her little fat arms—and she seemed to say,
  "I'm ready to go with you right away;
Don't hunt any more—take me."

I picked her off quick and kissed her,
And, hugging her to my breast,
  I heard a loud yelling that pierced me through,
  'Twas His Terrible Eminence, Grizzly-Gru,
Of the Monarchy of Unrest.

He had on a blood-red turban,
A picturesque lot of clothes,
  With big moustaches both fierce and black,
  And a ghastly saber to cut and hack,
And shoes that turned up at the toes.

Out of the gate of the garden
The cherub and I took flight,
  And closely behind us the saber flew,
  And back of the saber came Grizzly-Gru,
And he chased us all day till night.

I ran down the lunar crescent,
'And out on the silver horn;
I kissed the baby and held her tight,
And jumped down into the starry night,
And—I lit on the earth at morn.

He fitfully threw his saber,
It missed and went round the sun;
He followed no further, he was not rash,
But the baby held on to my coarse moustache,
'And seemed to enjoy the fun.

In saving that blue-eyed baby
From the gardens of Grizzly-Gru,
I suffered a terrible shock and fright;
But the doctor believes it will be all right,
'And he thinks he can pull me through.

# JOHN HENRY IN A STREET CAR

BY HUGH McHUGH

Throw me in the cellar and batten down the hatches.

I'm a wreck in the key of G flat.

I side-stepped in among a bunch of language-heavers yesterday and ever since I've been sitting on the ragged edge with my feet hanging over.

I was on my way down to Wall Street to help J. Pierpont Morgan buy a couple of railroads and all the world seemed as blithe and gay as a love clinch from Laura Jean Libbey's latest.

When I climbed into the cable-car I felt like a man who had mailed money to himself the night before.

I was aces.

And then somebody blew out my gas.

At the next corner two society flash-lights flopped in and sat next to me.

They had a lot of words they wanted to use and they started in.

The car stopped and two more of the 400's leading ladies jumped the hurdles and came down the aisle.

They sat on the other side of me.

In a minute they began to bite the dictionary.

Their efforts aroused the energies of three women who sat opposite me, and *they* proceeded to beat the English language black and blue.

In a minute the air was so full of talk that the grip germs had to pull out on the platform and chew the conductor.

The next one to me on my left started in:

"Oh, yes; we discharged our cook day before yesterday, but there's another coming this evening, and so—"

Her friend broke away and was up and back to the center with this:

"I was coming down Broadway this morning and I saw Julia Marlowe's leading man. I'm sure it was him, because I saw the show once in Chicago and he has the loveliest eyes I ever looked at!"

I knew that that was my cue to walk out, kick the motorman in the knuckles, upset the car and send in a fire call, but I passed it up.

I just sat there and bit my nails like the heavy villain . in one of Corse Payton's ten, twen, thir dramas.

That "loveliest eyes" speech had me groggy.

Whenever I hear a woman turn on that "loveliest eyes" gag about an actor I always feel that a swift slap from a wet dish-rag would look well on her back hair.

Then the bunch across the aisle got the flag.

"Well, you know," says the broad lady who paid for one seat and was compelled by Nature to use three, "you know there's only five in our family, and so I take just five slices of stale bread and have a bowl of water ready in which I've dropped a pinch of salt. Then I take a piece of butter about the size of a walnut, and thoroughly grease the bottom of a frying-pan; then beat five eggs to a froth, and—"

I'm hoping the conductor will come in and give us all a tip to take to the timber because the cops are going to pinch the room, but there's nothing doing.

One of the dames on my right finds her voice and passes it around:—

"Oh, I think it's a perfect fright! I always did detest electric blue, anyway. It is so unbecoming, and then—"

I've just decided that this lady ought to make up as a Swede servant girl and play the part, when her friend hooks in:

"Oh, yes; I think it will look perfectly sweet! It is a foulard in one of those new heliotrope tints, made with a crêpe de chine chemisette, with a second vest peeping out on either side of the front over an embroidered satin vest and cut in scallops on the edge, finished with a full ruche of white chiffon, and the sleeves are just too tight for any use, and the skirt is too long for any good, and I declare the lining is too sweet! and I just hate to wear it out on the street and get it soiled, and I was going to have it made with a tunic, and Mrs. Wigwag—that's my brother-in-law's first cousin—she had her's made to wear with guimpes—and they are so economical! and—"

Think of a guy having to ride four miles and get his forehead fanned all the while with talk about foulard and crêpe de chine and guimpes!

Wouldn't it lead you to a padded cell?

Say! I was down and out—no kidding!

I wanted to get up and fight the door-tender, but I couldn't.

One of the conversationalists was sitting on my overcoat.

I felt that if I got up and called my coat back to Papa she might lose the thread of her story, and the jar would be something frightful.

So I sat still and saved her life.

The one on my right must have been the Lady President of The Hammer Club.

She was talking about some other girl and she didn't do a thing to the absent one.

She said she was svelte.

I suppose that's Dago for a shine.

That's the way with some women. They can't come right out and call another woman a polish. They have to beat around the bush and chase their friends to the swamps by throwing things like "svelte" at them. Tush!

I tried to duck the foreign tattle on my right and by so doing I'm next to this on my left:

"Oh, yes; I think politics is just too lovely! I don't know whether I'd rather be a Democrat or a Republican, but I think—oh! just look at the hat that woman has on! Isn't that a fright? Wonder if she trimmed it herself. Of course she did; you can tell by—"

I'm gasping for breath when the broad lady across the aisle gets the floor:

"No, indeed! I didn't have Eliza vaccinated. Why, she's too small yet, and don't you know my sister's husband's brother's child was vaccinated, and she is younger than our Eliza, but I don't just care, I don't want—"

Then the sweet girlish thing on my left gave me the corkscrew jab.

It was the finish:

"Isn't that lovely? Well, as I was telling you, Charlie came last night and brought Mr. Storeclose with him. Mr. Storeclose is awfully nice. He plays the mandolin just too sweet for anything, and—"

Me!—to the oyster beds! No male impersonators garroting a mandolin—not any in mine!

When I want to take a course in music I'll climb into a public library and read how Baldy Sloane wrote the Tiger Lily with one hand tied behind him and his feet on the piano.

So I fell off the car and crawled home to mother.

# THE MUSKEETER

BY JOSH BILLINGS

Muskeeters are a game bug, but they won't bite at a hook. Thare iz millyuns ov them kaught every year, but not with a hook, this makes the market for them unstiddy, the supply allways exceeding the demand. The muskeeto iz born on the sly, and cums to maturity quicker than enny other ov the domestik animiles. A muskeeter at 3 hours old iz just az reddy and anxious to go into bizzness for himself, az ever he iz, and bites the fust time az sharp, and natral, as red pepper duz. The muskeeter haz a good ear for musik, and sings without notes. The song ov the muskeeto iz monotonous to sum folks, but in me it stirs up the memorys ov other days. I hav lade awake, all nite long, menny a time and listened to the sweet anthems ov the muskeeter. I am satisfied that thare want nothing made in vain, but i kant help thinking how mighty kluss the musketoze kum to it. The muskeeter haz inhabited this world since its kreashun, and will probably hang around here until bizzness closes. Whare the muskeeter goes to in the winter iz a standing konumdrum, which all the naturalists hav giv up, but we kno he dont go far, for he iz on hand early each year with hiz probe fresh ground, and polished. Muskeeters must be one ov the luxurys ov life, they certainly aint one ov the necessarys, not if we kno ourselfs.

# THE TURNINGS OF A BOOKWORM

BY CAROLYN WELLS

Love levels all plots.
Dead men sell no tales.
A new boom sweeps clean.
Circumstances alter bookcases.
The more haste the less read.
Too many books spoil the trade.
Many hands make light literature.
Epigrams cover a multitude of sins.
Ye can not serve Art and Mammon.
A little sequel is a dangerous thing.
It's a long page that has no turning.
Don't look a gift-book in the binding.
A gilt-edged volume needs no accuser.
In a multitude of characters there is safety.
Incidents will happen even in the best regulated novels.
One touch of Nature makes the whole book sell.
Where there's a will there's a detective story.
A book in the hand is worth two in the library.
An ounce of invention is worth a pound of style.
A good name is rather to be chosen than great characters.
Where there's so much puff, there must be some buyer.

# THE FEAST OF THE MONKEYS

BY JOHN PHILIP SOUSA

In days of old,
So I've been told,
The monkeys gave a feast.
They sent out cards,
With kind regards,
To every bird and beast.
The guests came dressed,
In fashion's best,
Unmindful of expense;
Except the whale,
Whose swallowtail,
Was "soaked" for fifty cents.

The guests checked wraps,
Canes, hats and caps;
And when that task was done,
The footman he
With dignitee,
Announced them one by one.
In Monkey Hall,
The host met all,
And hoped they'd feel at ease,
"I scarcely can,"
Said the Black and Tan,
"I'm busy hunting fleas."

"While waiting for
A score or more
Of guests," the hostess said,
"We'll have the Poodle
Sing *Yankee Doodle,*
A-standing on his head.
And when this through,
Good Parrot, you,
Please show them how you swear."
"Oh, dear; don't cuss,"
Cried the Octopus,
And he walked off on his ear.

The Orang-Outang
A sea-song sang,
About a Chimpanzee
Who went abroad,
In a drinking gourd,
To the coast of Barberee.
Where he heard one night,
When the moon shone bright,
A school of mermaids pick
Chromatic scales
From off their tails,
And did it mighty slick.

"All guests are here,
To eat the cheer,
And dinner's served, my Lord."
The butler bowed;
And then the crowd
Rushed in with one accord.
The fiddler-crab
Came in a cab,

And played a piece in C;
While on his horn,
The Unicorn
Blew, *You'll Remember Me.*

"To give a touch
Of early Dutch
To this great feast of feasts,
I'll drink ten drops
Of Holland's schnapps,"
Spoke out the King of Beasts.
"That must taste fine,"
Said the Porcupine,
"Did you see him smack his lip?"
"I'd smack mine, too,"
Cried the Kangaroo,
"If I didn't have the pip."

The Lion stood,
And said: "Be good
Enough to look this way;
Court Etiquette
Do not forget,
And mark well what I say:
My royal wish
Is ev'ry dish
Be tasted first by me."
"Here's where I smile,"
Said the Crocodile,
And he climbed an axle-tree.

The soup was brought,
And quick as thought,
The Lion ate it all.

"You can't beat that,"
Exclaimed the Cat,
"For monumental gall."
"The soup," all cried.
"Gone," Leo replied,
" 'Twas just a bit too thick."
"When we get through,"
Remarked the Gnu,
"I'll hit him with a brick."

The Tiger stepped,
Or, rather, crept,
Up where the Lion sat.
"O, mighty boss
I'm at a loss
To know where I am at.
I came to-night
With appetite
To drink and also eat;
As a Tiger grand,
I now demand,
I get there with both feet."

The Lion got
All-fired hot
And in a passion flew.
"Get out," he cried,
"And save your hide,
You most offensive *You*."
"I'm not afraid,"
The Tiger said,
"I know what I'm about."
But the Lion's paw
Reached the Tiger's jaw,
And he was good and out.

The salt-sea smell
Of Mackerel,
Upon the air arose;
Each hungry guest
Great joy expressed,
And "sniff!" went every nose.
With glutton look
The Lion took
The spiced and sav'ry dish.
Without a pause
He worked his jaws,
And gobbled all the fish.

Then ate the roast,
The quail on toast,
The pork, both fat and lean;
The jam and lamb,
The potted ham,
And drank the kerosene.
He raised his voice:
"Come, all rejoice,
You've seen your monarch dine."
"Never again,"
Clucked the Hen,
And all sang *Old Lang Syne*.

# THE BILLVILLE SPIRIT MEETING

BY FRANK L. STANTON

We had a sperrit meetin' (we'll never have no more!)
To call up all the sperrits of them that's "gone before."
A feller called a "medium" (he wuz of medium size),
Took the contract fer the fetchin' o' them sperrits from the
    skies.

The mayor—the town council—the parson an' his wife,
Come to shake han's with them sperrits what had left the
    other life;
The Colonel an' the Major—the coroner, an' all
Wuz waitin' an' debatin' in the darkness o' the hall.

The medium roared, "Silence! Amanda Jones appears!
Is her husband present?" ("No, sir—he's been restin'
    twenty years!")
"Here's the ghost of Sally Spilkins, from the lan' whar'
    glories glow:
Would her husband like to see her?" (An' a feeble voice
    said, *"No!"*)

"Here's the wife of Colonel Buster; she wears a heavenly
    smile:
She wants to see the Colonel, an' she's comin' down the
    aisle!"
Then all wuz wild confusion—it warn't a bit o' fun!—
With "Lord, have mercy on me," the Colonel broke an'
    run!

188

Then the coroner got skeery an' scampered fer his life!
"Stop—stop him!" said the medium; "here comes his sec-
    ond wife!"
But thar' warn't a man could stop him in that whole
    blame settlement,—
He turned a double summersault an' out the winder
    went!

Then, the whole town council follered an' hollered all the
    way;
The parson said he had a call 'bout ten miles off, to pray!
He didn't preach nex' Sunday, an' they tell it roun' a bit,
Accordin' to the best reports the parson's runnin' yit!

# A CRY FROM THE CONSUMER

BY WILBUR D. NESBIT

Grasshoppers roam the Kansas fields and eat the tender
     grass—
A trivial affair, indeed, but what then comes to pass?
You go to buy a panama, or any other hat;
You learn the price has been advanced a lot because of
     that.
A glacier up in Canada has slipped a mile or two—
A little thing like this can boost the selling price of glue.
Occurrences so tragic always thrill me to the core;
I hope and pray that nothing ever happens any more.

Last week the peaceful Indians went a-searching after
     scalps,
And then there was an avalanche 'way over in the Alps;
These diametric happenings seem nothing much, but
     look—
We had to add a dollar to the wages of the cook.
The bean-crop down at Boston has grown measurably
     less,
And so the dealer charges more for goods to make a
     dress.
Each day there is some incident to make a man feel sore,
I'm on my knees to ask that nothing happens any more.

It didn't rain in Utah and it did in old Vermont—
Result: it costs you fifty more to take a summer's jaunt;
Upon the plains of Tibet some tornadoes took a roll—
Therefore the barons have to charge a higher price for
     coal.

A street-car strike in Omaha has cumulative shocks—
It boosted huckleberries up to twenty cents a box.
No matter what is happening it always finds your door—
Give us a rest! Let nothing ever happen any more.

Mosquitoes in New Jersey bite a magnate on the wing—
Result: the poor consumer feels that fierce mosquito's
  sting:
The skeeter's song is silenced, but in something like an
  hour
The grocers understand that it requires a raise in flour.
A house burns down in Texas and a stove blows up in
  Maine,
Ten minutes later breakfast foods in prices show a gain.
Effects must follow causes—which is what I most de-
  plore;
I hope and pray that nothing ever happens any more.

## A DISAPPOINTMENT

### BY JOHN BOYLE O'REILLY

Her hair was a waving bronze, and her eyes
  Deep wells that might cover a brooding soul;
And who, till he weighed it, could ever surmise
  That her heart was a cinder instead of a coal!

# THE BRITISH MATRON

BY NATHANIEL HAWTHORNE

I have heard a good deal of the tenacity with which English ladies retain their personal beauty to a late period of life; but (not to suggest that an American eye needs use and cultivation, before it can quite appreciate the charm of English beauty at any age) it strikes me that an English lady of fifty is apt to become a creature less refined and delicate, so far as her physique goes, than anything that we Western people class under the name of woman. She has an awful ponderosity of frame, not pulpy, like the looser development of our few fat women, but massive with solid beef and streaky tallow; so that (though struggling manfully against the idea) you inevitably think of her as made up of steaks and sirloins. When she walks, her advance is elephantine. When she sits down it is on a great round space of her Maker's footstool, where she looks as if nothing could ever move her. She imposes awe and respect by the muchness of her personality, to such a degree that you probably credit her with far greater moral and intellectual force than she can fairly claim. Her visage is usually grim and stern, seldom positively forbidding, yet calmly terrible, not merely by its breadth and weight of feature, but because it seems to express so much well-defined self-reliance, such acquaintance with the world, its toils, troubles, and dangers, and such sturdy capacity for trampling down a foe. Without anything positively salient, or actively offensive, or, indeed, unjustly formidable to her neighbors, she has the effect of a seventy-four-gun ship in time of peace; for, while you assure yourself that there is no real danger, you can not help thinking how tremendous would be her onset, if pugnaciously inclined, and how futile the effort to inflict any counter-injury. She certainly looks tenfold—nay, a hundredfold—better able to take care of herself than our slender-framed and haggard womankind; but I have not found reason to suppose that the English dowager of fifty has actually greater courage, fortitude, and strength of character than our women of similar age, or even a tougher physical endurance than they. Morally, she is strong, I suspect, only in society, and in the common routine of social affairs, and would be found powerless and timid in any exceptional strait that might call for energy outside of the conventionalities amid which she has grown up.

You can meet this figure in the street, and live, and even smile at the recollection. But conceive of her in a ball-room, with the bare, brawny arms that she invariably displays there, and all the other corresponding development, such as is beautiful in the maiden blossom, but a spectacle to howl at in such an over-blown cabbage-rose as this.

Yet, somewhere in this enormous bulk there must be hidden the modest, slender, violet-nature of a girl, whom an alien mass of earthliness has unkindly overgrown; for an English maiden in her teens, though very seldom so pretty as our own damsels, possesses, to say the truth, a certain charm of half-blossom, and delicately folded leaves, and tender womanhood, shielded by maidenly reserves, with which, somehow or other, our American girls often fail to adorn themselves during an appreciable moment. It is a pity that the English violet should grow into such an outrageously developed peony as I have attempted to describe. I wonder whether a middle-aged husband ought to be considered as legally married to all the accretions that have overgrown the slenderness of his bride, since he led her to the altar, and which make her so much more than he ever bargained for! Is it not a sounder view of the case, that the matrimonial bond can not be held to include the three-fourths of the wife that had no existence when the ceremony was performed? And as a matter of conscience and good morals, ought not an English married pair to insist upon the celebration of a silver wedding at the end of twenty-five years in order to legalize and mutually appropriate that corporeal growth of which both parties have individually come into possession since they were pronounced one flesh?

## THE TRAGEDY OF IT

BY ALDEN CHARLES NOBLE

Alas for him, alas for it,
    Alas for you and I!
When this I think I raise my mitt
    To dry my weeping eye.

# STAGE WHISPERS

BY CAROLYN WELLS

Deadheads tell no tales.
Stars are stubborn things.
All's not bold that titters.
Contracts make cowards of us all.
One good turn deserves an encore.
A little actress is a dangerous thing.
It's a long skirt that has no turning.
Stars rush in where angels fear to tread.
Managers never hear any good of themselves.
A manager is known by the company he keeps.
A plot is not without honor save in comic opera.
Take care of the dance and the songs will take care of themselves.

# THE PETTIBONE LINEAGE

BY JAMES T. FIELDS

My name is Esek Pettibone, and I wish to affirm in the outset that it is a good thing to be well-born. In thus connecting the mention of my name with a positive statement, I am not aware that a catastrophe lies coiled up in the juxtaposition. But I can not help writing plainly that I am still in favor of a distinguished family-tree. ESTO PERPETUA! To have had somebody for a great-grand-father that was somebody is exciting. To be able to look back on long lines of ancestry that were rich, but respectable, seems decorous and all right. The present Earl of Warwick, I think, must have an idea that strict justice has been done *him* in the way of being launched properly into the world. I saw the Duke of Newcastle once, and as the farmer in Conway described Mount Washington, I thought the Duke felt a propensity to "hunch up some." Somehow it is pleasant to dook down on the crowd and have a conscious right to do so.

Left an orphan at the tender age of four years, having no brothers or sisters to prop me round with young affections and sympathies, I fell into three pairs of hands, excellent in their way, but peculiar. Patience, Eunice, and Mary Ann Pettibone were my aunts on my father's side. All my mother's relations kept shady when the lonely orphan looked about for protection; but Patience Pettibone, in her stately way, said,—"The boy belongs to a good family, and he shall never want while his three

196

aunts can support him." So I went to live with my plain, but benignant protectors, in the state of New Hampshire.

During my boyhood the best-drilled lesson that fell to my keeping was this: "Respect yourself. We come of more than ordinary parentage. Superior blood was probably concerned in getting up the Pettibones. Hold your head erect, and some day you shall have proof of your high lineage."

I remember once, on being told that I must not share my juvenile sports with the butcher's three little beings, I begged to know why not. Aunt Eunice looked at Patience, and Mary Ann knew what she meant.

"My child," slowly murmured the eldest sister, "our family, no doubt, came of a very old stock; perhaps we belong to the nobility. Our ancestors, it is thought, came over laden with honors, and no doubt were embarrassed with riches, though the latter importation has dwindled in the lapse of years. Respect yourself, and when you grow up you will not regret that your old and careful aunt did not wish you to play with the butcher's offspring."

I felt mortified that I ever had a desire to "knuckle up" with any but kings' sons, or sultans' little boys. I longed to be among my equals in the urchin line, and fly my kite with only high-born youngsters.

Thus I lived in a constant scene of self-enchantment on the part of the sisters, who assumed all the port and feeling that properly belonged to ladies of quality. Patrimonial splendor to come danced before their dim eyes; and handsome settlements, gay equipages, and a general grandeur of some sort loomed up in the future for the American branch of the House of Pettibone.

It was a life of opulent self-delusion, which my aunts

were never tired of nursing; and I was too young to doubt the reality of it. All the members of our little household held up their heads, as if each said, in so many words, "There is no original sin in *our* composition, whatever of that commodity there may be mixed up with the common clay of Snowborough."

Aunt Patience was a star, and dwelt apart. Aunt Eunice looked at her through a determined pair of spectacles, and worshiped while she gazed. The youngest sister lived in a dreamy state of honors to come, and had constant zoölogical visions of lions, griffins, and unicorns, drawn and quartered in every possible style known to the Heralds' College. The Reverend Hebrew Bullet, who used to drop in quite often and drink several compulsory glasses of home-made wine, encouraged his three parishoners in their aristocratic notions, and extolled them for what he called their "stooping-down to every-day life." He differed with the ladies of our house only on one point. He contended that the unicorn of the Bible and the rhinoceros of to-day were one and the same animal. My aunts held a different opinion.

In the sleeping-room of my Aunt Patience reposed a trunk. Often during my childish years I longed to lift the lid and spy among its contents the treasures my young fancy conjured up as lying there in state. I dared not ask to have the cover raised for my gratification, as I had often been told I was "too little" to estimate aright what that armorial box contained. "When you grow up, you shall see the inside of it," Aunt Mary used to say to me; and so I wondered, and wished, but all in vain. I must have the virtue of *years* before I could view the treasures of past magnificence so long entombed in that wooden sarcophagus. Once I saw the faded sisters bending over the trunk together, and, as I thought, embalming something in camphor. Curiosity impelled me to linger, but, under some pretext, I was nodded out of the room.

Although my kinswomen's means were far from ample, they determined that Swiftmouth College should have the distinction of calling me one of her sons, and accordingly I was in due time sent for preparation to a neighboring academy. Years of study and hard fare in country boarding-houses told upon my self-importance as the descendant of a great Englishman, notwithstanding all my letters from the honored three came with counsel to "respect myself and keep up the dignity of the family." Growing-up man forgets good counsel. The Arcadia of respectability is apt to give place to the levity of football and other low-toned accomplishments. The book of life, at that period, opens readily at fun and frolic, and the insignia of greatness give the school-boy no envious pangs.

I was nineteen when I entered the hoary halls of Swiftmouth. I call them hoary, because they had been built more than fifty years. To me they seemed uncommonly hoary, and I snuffed antiquity in the dusty purlieus. I now began to study, in good earnest, the wisdom of the past. I saw clearly the value of dead men and mouldy precepts, especially if the former had been entombed a thousand years, and if the latter were well done in sounding Greek and Latin. I began to reverence royal lines of deceased monarchs, and longed to connect my own name, now growing into college popularity, with some far-off mighty one who had ruled in pomp and luxury his obsequious people. The trunk in Snowborough troubled my dreams. In that receptacle still slept the proof of our family distinction. "I will go," quoth I, "to the home of my aunts next vacation and there learn *how* we became mighty, and discover precisely why we don't practice to-day our inherited claims to glory."

I went to Snowborough. Aunt Patience was now anxious to lay before her impatient nephew the proof he burned to behold. But first she must explain. All the old family documents and letters were, no doubt, destroyed in the great fire of '98, as nothing in the shape of parchment or paper implying nobility had ever been discovered in Snowborough, or elsewhere. *But* there had been preserved, for many years, a suit of imperial clothes that had been worn by their great-grandfather in England, and, no doubt, in the New World also. These garments had been carefully watched and guarded, for were they not the proof that their owner belonged to a station in life second, if second at all, to the royal court of King George itself? Precious casket, into which I was soon to have the privilege of gazing! Through how many long years these fond, foolish virgins had lighted their unflickering lamps of expectation and hope at this cherished old shrine!

I was now on my way to the family repository of all our greatness. I went up stairs "on the jump." We all knelt down before the well-preserved box; and my proud Aunt Patience, in a somewhat reverent manner, turned the key. My heart,—I am not ashamed to confess it now, although it is forty years since the quartet, in search of family honors, were on their knees that summer afternoon in Snowborough,—my heart beat high. I was about to look on that which might be a duke's or an earl's regalia. And I was descended from the owner in a direct line! I had lately been reading Shakespeare's *Titus Andronicus;* and I remembered, there before the trunk, the lines:

> "O sacred receptacle of my joys,
> Sweet cell of virtue and nobility!"

The lid went up, and the sisters began to unroll the precious garments, which seemed all enshrined in aromatic gums and spices. The odor of that interior lives with me to this day; and I grow faint with the memory of that hour. With pious precision the clothes were uncovered, and at last the whole suit was laid before my expectant eyes.

Reader! I am an old man now, and have not long to walk this planet. But whatever dreadful shock may be in reserve for my declining years, I am certain I can bear it; for I went through that scene at Snowborough, and still live!

When the garments were fully displayed, all the aunts looked at me. I had been to college; I had studied Burke's *Peerage;* I had been once to New York. Perhaps I could immediately name the exact station in noble British life to which that suit of clothes belonged. I could; I saw it all at a glance. I grew flustered and pale. I dared not look my poor deluded female relatives in the face.

"What rank in the peerage do these gold-laced garments and big buttons betoken?" cried all three.

*"It is a suit of servant's livery!"* gasped I, and fell back with a shudder.

That evening, after the sun had gone down, we buried those hateful garments in a ditch at the bottom of the garden. Rest there perturbed body-coat, yellow trousers, brown gaiters, and all!

"Vain pomp and glory of this world, I hate ye!"

# WHY MOLES HAVE HANDS

BY ANNE VIRGINIA CULBERTSON

One day the children came running to Aunt Nancy
with a mole which one of the dogs had just killed. They
had never seen one before and were very curious as to
what it might be.

"Well, befo' de king!" said Nancy, "whar y'all bin
livin' dat you nuver seed a mole befo'? Whar you come
f'um mus' be a mighty cur'ous spot ef dey ain' have
no moleses dar; mus' be sump'n wrong wid dat place.
I bin mos' all over dish yer Sussex kyounty endurin' er
my time, an' I ain' nuver come 'cross no place yit whar
dey ain' have moleses.

"Moleses is sut'n'y cur'ous li'l creeturs," she continued. "I bin teckin' tickler notuss un 'em dis long time,
an' dey knows mo'n you'd think fer, jes' ter look at 'em.
Dough dey lives down un'need de groun', yit dey is fus'-
class swimmers; I done seed one, wid my own eyes,
crossin' de branch, an' dey kin root 'long un'need de
yearf mos' ez fas' ez a hoss kin trot on top uv hit. Y'all
neenter look dat-a-way, 'kase hit's de trufe; dey's jes'
built fer gittin' 'long fas' unner groun'. Der han's is
bofe pickaxes an' shovels fer 'em; dey digs an' scoops
wid der front ones an' kicks de dirt out de way wid der
behime ones. Der strong snouts he'ps 'em, too, ter push
der way thu de dirt."

"Their fur is just as soft and shiny as silk," said
Janey.

"Yas," said Aunt Nancy, "hit's dat sof' an' shiny dat,

202

dough dey live all time in de dirt, not a speck er dirt sticks to 'em. You ses 'sof' an' shiny ez silk,' but I tell you hit *is* silk; silk clo'es, dat 'zackly w'at 'tis."

Ned laughed. "Who ever heard of an animal dressed in silk clothes?" he said.

"Nemmine," she answered, "you talks mighty peart, but I knows w'at I knows, an' dish yer I bin tellin' you is de sho'-'nuff trufe."

"Just see its paws," Janey went on, "why, they look exactly like hands."

"Look lak *han's! look* lak han's! umph! dey *is* han's, all thumbered an' fingered jes lak yo'n; an', w'at's mo', dey wuz onct human han's; *human,* dey wuz so!"

"How could they ever have been human hands and then been put on a mole's body?" asked Ned. "I believe most things you say, Aunt Nancy, but I can't swallow that."

"Dar's a li'l boy roun' dese diggin's whar talkin' mighty sassy an' rambunkshus, seem ter me. I ain' ax you ter swoller nuttin' 't all, but 'pears ter me y'all bin swollerin' dem 'ar ol' tales right an' lef', faster'n' I kin call 'em ter min', an' I ain' seed none er you choke on 'em yit, ner cry, 'nuff said. I'se 'tickler saw'y 'bout dis, 'kase I done had hit in min' ter tell you a tale 'bout huccome moleses have han'ses, whar I larn f'um a ooman dat come f'um Fauquier kyounty, but now dat Mars' Ned 'pear ter be so jubous 'bout hit, I ain' gwine was'e my time on folks whar ain' gwine b'lieve me, no-hows. Nemmine, de chillen over on de Thompson place gwine baig me fer dat tale w'en I goes dar ag'in, an', w'at's mo', dey gwine git hit; fer dey b'lieves ev'y wu'd dat draps f'um my mouf, lak 'twuz de law an' de gospil."

Of course, the children protested that they were as ready to hang upon her words as the Thompson children

could possibly be, and presented their prior claim to the
tale in such moving fashion that Aunt Nancy was finally
prevailed upon to come down from her high horse and
tell the story.

"I done tol' you," she said, "dat dem 'ar han's is
human, an' I mean jes' w'at I ses, 'kase de moleses useter
be folks, sho'-'nuff folks, dough dey is all swunk up ter
dis size an' der han's is all dat's lef' ter tell de tale.
Yas, suh, in de ol' days, so fur back dat you kain't
kyount hit, de moleses wuz folks, an' mighty proud an'
biggitty folks at dat. Dey wan't gwine be ketched wear-
in' any er dish yer kaliker, er linsey-woolsey, er homespun er sech ez dat, ner even broadclawf, ner bombazine,
naw suh! Dey jes' tricked derse'fs out in de fines' an'
shinies' er silk, nuttin' mo' ner less, an' den dey went
a-traipsin' up an' down an' hether an' yon, fer tu'rr folks
ter look at an' mek 'miration over. Mo'n dat, dey 'uz
so fine an' fiddlin' dey oon set foot ter de groun' lessen
dar wuz a kyarpet spread down fer 'em ter walk on. Dey
tells me hit sut'n'y wuz a sight in de worl' ter see dem
'ar folks walkin' up an' down on de kyarpets, trailin'
an' rus'lin' der silk clo'es, an' curchyin' an' bobbin' ter
one nu'rr w'en dey met up, but nuver speakin' ter de
common folks whar walkin' on de groun', ner even so
much ez lookin' at 'em. W'ats mo', dey wuz so uppish
dey thought de yearf wuz too low down fer 'em even ter
run der eyes over, so dey went 'long wid der haids
r'ared an' der eyes all time lookin' up, stidder down.
You kin be sho' dem gwines-on ain' mek 'em pop'lous
wid tu'rr folks, 'kase people jes' natchelly kain't stan' hit
ter have you th'owin' up to 'em dat you is better'n w'at
dey is, w'en all de time dey knows you're nuttin' but
folks, same 'z dem.

"Dey kep' gwine on so-fashion, an' gittin' mo' an' mo'

pompered an' uppish, 'twel las' dey 'tracted de 'tention er de Lawd, an' He say ter Hisse'f, He do, 'Who is dese yer folks, anyhows, whar gittin' so airish, walkin' up an' down an' back an' fo'th on my yearf an' spurnin' hit so's't dey spread kyarpets 'twix' hit an' der footses, treatin' my yearf, w'at I done mek, lak 'twuz de dirt un'need der footses, an' 'spisin' der feller creeturs an' excusin' 'em er bein' common, an' keepin' der eyes turnt up all de time, ez ef dey wuz too good ter look at de things I done mek an' putt on my yearf? I mus' see 'bout dis; I mus' punish dese 'sumptious people an' show 'em dat one'r my creeturs is jez' ez low down ez tu'rr, in my sight.'

"So de Lawd He pass jedgment on de moleses. Fus' He tuck an' made 'em lose der human shape an' den He swunk 'em up ontwel dey 'z no bigger'n dey is now, dat 'uz ter show 'em how no-kyount dey wuz in His sight. Den bekase dey thought derse'fs too good ter walk 'pun de bare groun' He sont 'em ter live un'need hit, whar dey hatter dig an' scratch der way 'long. Las' uv all He tuck an' tuck 'way der eyes an' made 'em blin', dat's 'kase dey done 'spise ter look at der feller creeturs. But He feel kind er saw'y fer 'em w'en He git dat fur, an' He ain' wanter punish 'em too haivy, so He lef' 'em dese silk clo'es whar I done tol' you 'bout, an' dese han's whar you kin see fer yo'se'fs is human, an' I reckon bofe dem things putt 'em in min' er w'at dey useter be an' mek 'em 'umble. Uver sence den de moleses bin gwine 'long un'need de groun', 'cordin ter de jedgmen' er de Lawd, an' diggin' an' scratchin' der way thu de worl', in trial an' tribilashun, wid dem po' li'l human han'ses. An' dat orter l'arn you w'at comes er folks 'spisin' der fel-ler creeturs, an' I want y'all ter 'member dat nex' time I year you call dem Thompson chillen 'trash.' "

# WHY MOLES HAVE HANDS

"I'd like to know what use moles are," said Ned, who was of rather an investigating turn of mind; "they just go round rooting through the ground spoiling people's gardens, and I don't see what they're good for; you can't eat them or use them any way."

"Sho', chil'!" said Aunt Nancy, "you dunno w'at you talkin' 'bout; de Lawd have some use fer ev'y creetur He done mek. Dey tells me dat de moleses eats up lots er bugs an' wu'ms an' sech ez dat, dat mought hurt de craps ef dey wuz let ter live. Sidesen dat, jes' gimme one'r de claws er dat mole, an' lemme hang hit roun' de neck uv a baby whar cuttin' his toofs, an' I boun' you, ev'y toof in his jaws gwine come bustin' thu his goms widout nair' a ache er a pain ter let him know dey's dar. Don't talk ter me 'bout de moleses bein' wufless! I done waik de flo' too much wid cryin' babies not ter know de use er moleses."

"You don't really believe that, do you?" asked Ned.

"B'lieve hit!" she answered indignantly; "I don' *b'lieve* hit, I *knows* hit. I done tol' you all de things a hyar's foot kin do; w'ats de reason a mole's foot ain' good fer sump'n, too? Ef folks on'y knowed mo' about sech kyores ez dat dar neenter be so much sickness an' mis'ry in de worl'. I done kyored myse'f er de rheumatiz in my right arm jes' by tyin' a eel-skin roun' hit, an' ev'yb'dy on dis plantation knows dat ef you'll wrop a chil's hya'r wid eel-skin strings hit's boun' ter mek hit grow. Ef you want de chil' hisse'f ter grow an' ter walk soon you mus' bresh his feet wid de broom. I oon tell you dis ef I hadn't tried 'em myse'f. You mus'n' talk so biggitty 'bout w'at you dunno nuttin' 't all about. You come f'um up Norf yonner, an' mebbe dese things don' wu'k de same dar ez w'at dey does down yer whar we bin 'pendin' on 'em so long.'

# A PSALM OF LIFE

BY PHŒBE CARY

Tell me not, in idle jingle,
   Marriage is an empty dream,
For the girl is dead that's single,
   And things are not what they seem.

Married life is real, earnest,
   Single blessedness a fib,
Taken from man, to man returnest,
   Has been spoken of the rib.

Not enjoyment, and not sorrow,
   Is our destined end or way;
But to act, that each to-morrow
   Nearer brings the wedding-day.

Life is long, and youth is fleeting,
   And our hearts, if there we search,
Still like steady drums are beating
   Anxious marches to the Church.

In the world's broad field of battle,
   In the bivouac of life,
Be not like dumb, driven cattle;
   Be a woman, be a wife!

Trust no Future, howe'er pleasant!
   Let the dead Past bury its dead!
Act—act in the living Present.
   Heart within, and Man ahead!

# A PSALM OF LIFE

Lives of married folks remind us
  We can live our lives as well,
And, departing, leave behind us;—
  Such examples as will tell;—

Such examples, that another,
  Sailing far from Hymen's port,
A forlorn, unmarried brother,
  Seeing, shall take heart, and court.

Let us then be up and doing,
  With the heart and head begin;
Still achieving, still pursuing,
  Learn to labor, and to win!

# AN ODYSSEY OF K'S

BY WILBUR D. NESBIT

I've traveled up and down this land
   And crossed it in a hundred ways,
But somehow can not understand
   These towns with names chock-full of K's.
For instance, once it fell to me
   To pack my grip and quickly go—
I thought at first to Kankakee
   But then remembered Kokomo.
"Oh, Kankakee or Kokomo,"
I sighed, "just which I do not know."

Then to the ticket man I went—
   He was a snappy man, and bald,
Behind an iron railing pent—
   And I confessed that I was stalled.
"A much K'd town is booked for me,"
   I said. "I'm due to-morrow, so
I wonder if it's Kankakee
   Or if it can be Kokomo."
"There's quite a difference," growled he,
" 'Twixt Kokomo and Kankakee."

He spun a yard of tickets out—
   The folded kind that makes a strip
And leaves the passenger in doubt
   When the conductor takes a clip.

He flipped the tickets out, I say,
   And asked: "Now, which one shall it be?
I'll sell you tickets either way—
   To Kokomo or Kankakee."
And still I really did not know—
I thought it might be Kokomo.


At any rate, I took a chance;
   He struck his stamp-machine a blow
And I, a toy of circumstance,
   Was ticketed for Kokomo.
Upon the train I wondered still
   If all was right as it should be.
Some mystic warning seemed to fill
   My mind with thoughts of Kankakee.
The car-wheels clicked it out: "Now, he
Had better be for Kankakee!"


Until at last it grew so loud,
   At some big town I clambered out
And elbowed madly through the crowd,
   Determined on the other route.
The ticket-agent saw my haste;
   "Where do you wish to go?" cried he.
I yelled: "I have no time to waste—
   Please fix me up for Kankakee!"
Again the wheels, now fast, now slow,
Clicked: "Ought to go to Kokomo!"


Well, anyhow, I did not heed
   The message that they sent to me.
I went, and landed wrong indeed—
   Went all the way to Kankakee.

Then, in a rush, I doubled back—
　　Went wrong again, I'd have you know.
There was no call for me, alack!
　　Within the town of Kokomo.

And then I learned, confound the luck,
I should have gone to *Keokuk!*

# THE DEACON'S TROUT

BY HENRY WARD BEECHER

He was a curious trout. I believe he knew Sunday
just as well as Deacon Marble did. At any rate, the
deacon thought the trout meant to aggravate him. The
deacon, you know, is a little waggish. He often tells
about that trout. Sez he, "One Sunday morning, just as
I got along by the willows, I heard an awful splash, and
not ten feet from shore I saw the trout, as long as my
arm, just curving over like a bow, and going down with
something for breakfast. Gracious! says I, and I almost
jumped out of the wagon. But my wife Polly, says she,
'What on airth are you thinkin' of, Deacon? It's Sab-
bath day, and you're goin' to meetin'! It's a pretty business for a deacon!' That sort o' cooled me off. But I do
say that, for about a minute, I wished I wasn't a deacon.
But 't wouldn't made any difference, for I came down
next day to mill on purpose, and I came down once or
twice more, and nothin' was to be seen, tho' I tried him
with the most temptin' things. Wal, next Sunday I came
along ag'in, and, to save my life I couldn't keep off worldly
and wanderin' thoughts. I tried to be sayin' my catechism,
but I couldn't keep my eyes off the pond as we came up
to the willows. I'd got along in the catechism, as smooth
as the road, to the Fourth Commandment, and was sayin'
it out loud for Polly, and jist as I was sayin: *'What is required in the Fourth Commandment?'* I heard a splash,
and there was the trout, and, afore I could think, I said:

'Gracious, Polly, I must have that trout.' She almost riz right up, 'I knew you wa'n't sayin' your catechism hearty. Is this the way you answer the question about keepin' the Lord's day? I'm ashamed, Deacon Marble,' says she. 'You'd better change your road, and go to meetin' on the road over the hill. If I was a deacon, I wouldn't let a fish's tail whisk the whole catechism out of my head'; and I had to go to meetin' on the hill road all the rest of the summer."

## ENOUGH*

### BY TOM MASSON

I shot a rocket in the air,
It fell to earth, I knew not where
Until next day, with rage profound,
The man it fell on came around.
In less time than it takes to tell,
He showed me where that rocket fell;
And now I do not greatly care
To shoot more rockets in the air.

* By permission of Life Publishing Company.

# THE FIGHTING RACE

BY JOSEPH I. C. CLARKE

"Read out the names!" and Burke sat back,
    And Kelly drooped his head,
While Shea—they call him Scholar Jack—
    Went down the list of the dead.
Officers, seamen, gunners, marines,
    The crews of the gig and yawl,
The bearded man and the lad in his teens,
    Carpenters, coal-passers—all.
Then knocking the ashes from out his pipe,
    Said Burke, in an off-hand way,
"We're all in that dead man's list, by Cripe!
    Kelly and Burke and Shea."
"Well, here's to the Maine, and I'm sorry for Spain!"
    Said Kelly and Burke and Shea.

"Wherever there's Kellys there's trouble," said
      Burke.
    "Wherever fighting's the game,
Or a spice of danger in grown man's work,"
    Said Kelly, "you'll find my name."
"And do we fall short," said Burke, getting mad,
    "When it's touch and go for life?"
Said Shea, "It's thirty-odd years, be dad,
    Since I charged to drum and fife
Up Marye's Heights, and my old canteen
    Stopped a Rebel ball on its way.

There were blossoms of blood on our sprigs of
    green—
  Kelly and Burke and Shea—
And the dead did n't brag." "Well, here 's to the
    flag !"
  Said Kelly and Burke and Shea.


"I wish 't was in Ireland, for there's the place,"
  Said Burke, "that we 'd die by right,
In the cradle of our soldier race,
  After one good stand-up fight.
My grandfather fell on Vinegar Hill,
  And fighting was not his trade;
But his rusty pike 's in the cabin still,
  With Hessian blood on the blade."
"Aye, aye," said Kelly, "the pikes were great
  When the word was 'Clear the way!'
We were thick on the roll in ninety-eight—
  Kelly and Burke and Shea."
"Well, here 's to the pike and the sword and the
    like !"
  Said Kelly and Burke and Shea.


And Shea, the scholar, with rising joy,
  Said "We were at Ramillies.
We left our bones at Fontenoy,
  And up in the Pyrenees,
Before Dunkirk, on Landen's plain,
  Cremona, Lille, and Ghent,
We 're all over Austria, France, and Spain,
  Wherever they pitched a tent.
We 've died for England from Waterloo
  To Egypt and Dargai;

And still there 's enough for a corps or crew,
  Kelly and Burke and Shea."
"Well, here is to good honest fighting blood!"
  Said Kelly and Burke and Shea.

"Oh, the fighting races don't die out,
  If they seldom die in bed,
For love is first in their hearts, no doubt,"
  Said Burke. Then Kelly said:
"When Michael, the Irish Archangel, stands,
  The angel with the sword,
And the battle-dead from a hundred lands
  Are ranged in one big horde,
Our line, that for Gabriel's trumpet waits,
  Will stretch tree deep that day,
From Jehoshaphat to the Golden Gates—
  Kelly and Burke and Shea."
  "Well, here 's thank God for the race and the
    sod!"
  Said Kelly and Burke and Shea.

# THE ORGAN

BY HENRY WARD BEECHER

At one of his week night lectures, Beecher was speaking about the building and equipping of new churches. After a few satirical touches about church architects and their work, he went on to ridicule the usual style of pulpit—the "sacred mahogany tub"—"plastered up against some pillar like a barn-swallow's nest." Then he passed on to the erection of the organ, and to the opening recital.

"The organ long expected has arrived, been unpacked, set up, and gloried over. The great players of the region round about, or of distant celebrity, have had the grand organ exhibition; and this magnificent instrument has been put through all its paces in a manner which has surprised every one, and, if it had had a conscious existence, must have surprised the organ itself most of all. It has piped, fluted, trumpeted, brayed, thundered. It has played so loud that everybody was deafened, and so soft that nobody could hear. The pedals played for thunder, the flutes languished and coquetted, and the swell died away in delicious suffocation, like one singing a sweet song under the bed-clothes. Now it leads down a stupendous waltz with full brass, sounding very much as if, in summer, a thunderstorm should play, 'Come, Haste to the Wedding,' or 'Moneymusk.' Then come marches, galops, and hornpipes. An organ playing hornpipes ought to have elephants as dancers.

"At length a fugue is rendered to show the whole scope

and power of the instrument. The theme, like a cautious rat, peeps out to see if the coast is clear; and, after a few hesitations, comes forth and begins to frisk a little, and run up and down to see what it can find. It finds just what it did not want, a purring tenor lying in ambush and waiting for a spring; and as the theme comes incautiously near, the savage cat of a tenor springs at it, misses its hold, and then takes after it with terrible earnestness. But the tenor has miscalculated the agility of the theme. All that it could do, with the most desperate effort, was to keep the theme from running back into its hole again; and so they ran up and down, around and around, dodging, eluding, whipping in and out of every corner and nook, till the whole organ was aroused, and the bass began to take part, but unluckily slipped and rolled downstairs, and lay at the bottom raving and growling in the most awful manner, and nothing could appease it. Sometimes the theme was caught by one part, and dangled for a moment, then with a snatch, another part took it and ran off exultant, until, unawares, the same trick was played on it; and, finally, all the parts, being greatly exercised in mind, began to chase each other promiscuously in and out, up and down, now separating and now rushing in full tilt together, until everything in the organ loses patience and all the 'stops' are drawn, and, in spite of all that the brave organist could do—who bobbed up and down, feet, hands, head and all—the tune broke up into a real row, and every part was clubbing every other one, until at length, patience being no longer a virtue, the organist, with two or three terrible crashes, put an end to the riot, and brought the great organ back to silence."

# MY GRANDMOTHER'S TURKEY-TAIL FAN

BY SAMUEL MINTURN PECK

It owned not the color that vanity dons
  Or slender wits choose for display;
Its beautiful tint was a delicate bronze,
  A brown softly blended with gray.
From her waist to her chin, spreading out without break,
  'Twas built on a generous plan:
The pride of the forest was slaughtered to make
  My grandmother's turkey-tail fan.

For common occasions it never was meant:
  In a chest between two silken cloths
'Twas kept safely hidden with careful intent
  In camphor to keep out the moths.
'Twas famed far and wide through the whole countryside,
  From Beersheba e'en unto Dan;
And often at meeting with envy 'twas eyed,
  My grandmother's turkey-tail fan.

Camp-meetings, indeed, were its chiefest delight.
  Like a crook unto sheep gone astray
It beckoned backsliders to re-seek the right,
  And exhorted the sinners to pray.
It always beat time when the choir went wrong,
  In psalmody leading the van.
Old Hundred, I know, was its favorite song—
  My grandmother's turkey-tail fan.

# MY GRANDMOTHER'S TURKEY-TAIL FAN

A fig for the fans that are made nowadays,
 Suited only to frivolous mirth!
A different thing was the fan that I praise,
 Yet it scorned not the good things of earth.
At bees and at quiltings 'twas aye to be seen;
 The best of the gossip began
When in at the doorway had entered serene
 My grandmother's turkey-tail fan.

Tradition relates of it wonderful tales.
 Its handle of leather was buff.
Though shorn of its glory, e'en now it exhales
 An odor of hymn-books and snuff.
Its primeval grace, if you like, you can trace:
 'Twas limned for the future to scan,
Just under a smiling gold-spectacled face,
 My grandmother's turkey-tail fan.

# How to Develop

# Self-Confidence

## in Speech and Manner

By GRENVILLE KLEISER

*Author of "How to Speak in Public"; "How to Develop Power and Personality in Speaking," etc.*

The purpose of this book is to inspire in men lofty ideals. It is particularly for those who daily defraud themselves because of doubt, fearthought, and foolish timidity.

Thousands of persons are held in physical and mental bondage, owing to lack of self-confidence. Distrusting themselves, they live a life of limited effort, and at last pass on without having realized more than a small part of their rich possessions. It is believed that this book will be of substantial service to those who wish to rise above mediocrity, and who feel within them something of their divine inheritance. It is commended with confidence to every ambitious man.

### CONTENTS

Preliminary Steps—Building the Will—The Cure of Self-Consciousness—The Power of Right Thinking—Sources of Inspiration—Concentration—Physical Basis—Finding Yourself—General Habits—The Man and the Manner—The Discouraged Man—Daily Steps in Self-Culture—Imagination and Initiative—Positive and Negative Thought—The Speaking Voice—Confidence in Business—Confidence in Society—Confidence in Public Speaking—Toward the Heights—Memory Passages that Build Confidence.

*12mo, Cloth. $1.25, net; by mail, $1.35*

## FUNK & WAGNALLS COMPANY, Publishers
### NEW YORK AND LONDON

# How to
# ARGUE AND WIN

IN CONVERSATION, IN SALESMANSHIP, IN COMMITTEE-
MEETINGS, IN JURY CASES, IN THE PULPIT, ON
THE ROSTRUM, IN DEBATING SOCIETIES.

## By GRENVILLE KLEISER
*Author of "How to Speak in Public," etc.*

IN this book will be found definite suggestions for training
the mind in accurate thinking and in the power of clear
and effective statement. It is the outcome of many years
of experience in teaching men "to think on their feet."
The aim throughout is practical, and the ultimate end is a
knowledge of successful argumentation.

## CONTENTS

Introductory—Truth and Facts—Clearness and Conciseness—The
Use of Words—The Syllogism—Faults—Personality—The Lawyer—
The Business Man—The Preacher—The Salesman—The Public
Speaker—Brief-Drawing—The Discipline of Debate—Tact—Cause
and Effect—Reading Habits—Questions for Solution—Specimens of
Argumentation—Golden Rules in Argumentation.

"Mr. Kleiser offers no panacea (as the title might seem to imply).
Logic will not make a dunce a philosopher, neither will it insure
success where success is not deserved. But what he does offer
the honest debater in this practical book, is to put him in possession
of those laws of argumentation which lie at the bottom of sound
reasoning, based on fact."—*Times-Dispatch*, Richmond, Va.

*12mo, Cloth. $1.25, net; by mail, $1.35*

## FUNK & WAGNALLS COMPANY, Publishers,
### NEW YORK AND LONDON